INTRODUCTION TO THE
DIFFERENTIAL EQUATIONS
OF PHYSICS

36

By

L. HOPF

Professor at the Aachen Institute of Technology

Translated by

WALTER NEF

Professor at the University of Fribourg, Switzerland

NEW YORK

DOVER PUBLICATIONS

Library of Congress Catalog Card Number: 48-3072

Manufactured in the United States of America

Dover Publications, Inc.
180 Varick Street
New York 14, N. Y.

CONTENTS

CHAPTER I

THE DIFFERENTIAL EQUATION AS AN EXPRESSION OF A LAW OF NATURE

1. Law of causality

Any differential equation expresses a relation between derivatives or between derivatives and given functions of the variables. It thus establishes a relation between the increments of certain quantities and these quantities themselves. This property of a differential equation makes it the natural expression of the principle of causality which is the foundation of exact natural science. The ancient Greeks established laws of nature in which certain relations between numbers (harmony of spheres) or certain shapes of bodies played a privileged rôle. The law was supposed to state something about a process as a whole, or about the complete shape of a body. In more recent times (Galileo, Newton, etc.) a different concept has been adopted. We do not try to establish a relation between all phases of a process immediately, but only between one phase and the next. A law of this type may express, for example, how a certain state will develop in the immediate future, or it may describe the influence of the state of a certain particle on the particles in the immediate neighbourhood. Thus we have a procedure for the description of a law of nature in terms of small (mathematically speaking, infinitesimal) differences of time and space. The increments with which the law is concerned appear as

1

derivatives, i.e., as the limits of the quotient of the increments of the variables which describe the process over the increment of space or time in which this development takes place. A law of nature of this form is the expression of the relation between one state and the neighbouring (in time or space) states and therefore represents a special form of the principle of causality.

2. Ordinary and partial differential equations

A differential equation is called ordinary if there is only one independent variable, and partial if there are several independent variables. In an ordinary differential equation only ordinary derivatives appear, while a partial differential equation contains partial derivatives. The difference between these two types of differential equations appears more significant from the standpoint of physics, and is related to the deepest physical problems. There exist two fundamentally different concepts of physical processes upon which physical theories are based. According to the first point of view, matter consists of single particles which move in space without undergoing any changes. The position of each particle is determinable as a function of time, the only independent variable of all processes. This point of view provides the foundation of Newtonian mechanics, of atomism, in which the motion of elementary particles is considered as the sole basis of all physical processes. The ordinary differential equation is the mathematical expression of laws of this kind, since there is only one independent variable, namely the time.

On the other hand we have the field theory in physics, employed particularly in the domains of electromagnetism and optics. In this theory, all processes are determined by field quantities which have a well defined value at each point of space. This value is usually a function of the time. We thus have four independent variables (the three space coordinates and the time). The laws which are based on this concept are expressed by partial differential equations.

Ordinary and partial differential equations are thus the mathematical expressions of the two fundamental points of view, the synthesis of which in quantum theory is one of the major problems of contemporary physics.

Ordinary differential equations may occur, however, in physical problems which have nothing to do with the atomistic point of view, e.g., in the theory of electrical oscillations or the bending of beams. But in these cases the ordinary differential equation is not a direct expression of any fundamental law, but rather an approximation which neglects the influence of all but one of the variables.

3. Initial and boundary conditions

The differential equation alone does not express a specific physical problem. It expresses the general law under consideration, but not the specific case. A specific case is defined by initial or boundary conditions. Any integration implies arbitrary constants and, moreover, the integration of a partial differential equation involves arbitrary functions. In order to formulate the problem completely in mathematical terms and to solve the differential equation, there must be given as many physical boundary conditions as there are arbitrary functions or constants in the integrated equation. In the following, we shall always be careful about the necessary number of conditions.

4. Scalars and vectors

The mathematical quantities which are used to describe a physical quantity or a process are of different kinds. They differ principally in the number of numerical values which are required for their determination. A quantity which can be completely determined by only one number is called a scalar (e.g., temperature, density, time.) Before we can specify this single number, we must, of course, choose a system of units.

The position of a point in space, however, can not be determined by a single number, but must be given by three of them, since the space has three dimensions. The manner in which the three numbers are determined is not important. They may be the coordinates of the point in a rectangular coordinate system, or the distance of the point from a fixed origin and two other numbers which determine the direction from the origin to the point. In any case, we must use three numbers in order to determine the position of a point in space. There exist many quantities which can be characterized by a line segment in three-dimensional space as, for instance, the forces in problems of graphical statics. Any such quantity which is determined by three numbers is called a vector.

There exist many complicated physical quantities which require more than three numbers for their determination (e.g., the stress and the strain in an elastic body, each of which is defined by six numbers). Quantities of this kind are called tensors. In general tensor theory, vectors appear as tensors of the first order, while scalars are tensors of the zero-th order. In modern physics, other quantities exist which can be represented as segments in a four-dimensional space. They are called four-dimensional vectors. Furthermore, there exist four-dimensional tensors, etc. We shall be concerned here only with scalars and vectors (3-dimensional).

The limited space which is at our disposal in this book does not allow us to enter into the deeper special problems of physics, so that even the most elementary cases of wave mechanics and the theory of relativity cannot be presented. As tools we shall use only the fundamental theorems of differential and integral calculus. This introduction strives for a close connection between the physical concepts and their mathematical formulation. As a basis for further studies we suggest the book: *Die Differential- und Integralgleichungen der Mechanik und Physik* by Ph. Frank and R. von Mises.[1]

[1] 2nd ed., Photo-reprint, M. S. Rosenberg, New York, 1945.

CHAPTER II

THE ORDINARY DIFFERENTIAL EQUATIONS OF THE MECHANICS OF PARTICLES

1. The motion of a particle

The elementary unit of mechanics is the particle, the physical behaviour of which is completely determined by its mass m which is an invariable scalar quantity, and by its position in space which depends on the time and which may be described by the rectangular coordinates x, y, z. The quantities x, y, z are the components of a vector $\mathbf{r}$, which is drawn from the origin of the coordinate system to the point x, y, z. The only independent variable is the time t.

The motion of a particle is described by two quantities which represent the change in the position of the particle in a very short interval of time by means of a limiting process. To begin with, let the point move along the x-axis, so that $y = 0$ and $z = 0$ at every instant. If we designate the x-coordinate at the time t by x and that at time t_1 by x_1, then the ratio (difference of position)/(difference of time) $= (x_1 - x)/(t_1 - t)$ is called the "average velocity" in the interval $(t_1 - t)$, and the limit dx/dt the "instantaneous velocity" at the time t or just the "speed" v. The speed is usually not a constant, but depends on the time. If one forms the ratio (difference of speed)/(difference of time) and then proceeds to the limit for $(t_1 - t) \to 0$, one obtains the "acceleration" $b = dv/dt = d^2x/dt^2$.

If the motion does not have a fixed direction, so that y and z can also be different from 0, we obtain three components of the velocity by the same limit processes

$$v_x = \frac{dx}{dt}, \qquad v_y = \frac{dy}{dt}, \qquad v_z = \frac{dz}{dt} \qquad (2.1)$$

and three components of acceleration

$$b_x = \frac{dv_x}{dt} = \frac{d^2x}{dt^2}, \; b_y = \frac{dv_y}{dt} = \frac{d^2y}{dt^2}, \; b_z = \frac{dv_z}{dt} = \frac{d^2z}{dt^2}. \quad (2.2)$$

Thus velocity and acceleration are also vectors, and as such will be designated by the bold-face letters $\mathbf{v}$ and $\mathbf{b} = d\mathbf{v}/dt$.

The fundamental law of Newton constitutes a relation between the "acceleration" vector and the "force" vector $\mathbf{P}$ which acts on the particle. The law is expressed by the differential equation,

$$m \frac{d\mathbf{v}}{dt} = \mathbf{P} \qquad (2.3)$$

or in component form by

$$m \frac{d^2x}{dt^2} \left(= m \frac{dv_x}{dt} \right) = P_x \, , \qquad m \frac{d^2y}{dt^2} = P_y \, ,$$

$$\qquad (2.3a)$$

$$m \frac{d^2z}{dt^2} = P_z \, .$$

In this book it is not possible to discuss all the physical and philosophical problems which are connected with the conceptions of "force" and "mass". Our only guide is the intuition we develop from everyday experiences in moving heavy masses, stretching elastic ropes, etc., by muscular exertion. The nature of a force as a vector having direction as well as magnitude is apparent in these actions. Any force causes a change of velocity and consequently a change of position. These changes are expressed as derivatives. The law, therefore, has the form of a differential equation.

2. Free fall

In order to pass from the general law of nature to a specific case, we take a body which is under the influence of gravity only, such that the sole force acting on it is its weight G. This weight acts in a certain direction, "downwards". We take the negative y-axis in this direction. Then the three components of the force are

$$P_x = 0, \qquad P_y = -G, \qquad P_z = 0, \qquad (2.4)$$

and we have the differential equations of the problem

$$m \frac{d^2x}{dt^2} = 0, \qquad m \frac{d^2y}{dt^2} = -G, \qquad m \frac{d^2z}{dt^2} = 0. \quad (2.5)$$

Our task is to determine the three quantities x, y, z as functions of t. For this purpose we require additional information so that the special case under consideration becomes separated from all the others enabling us to determine the constants of integration.

We have three differential equations of the second order, i.e., equations in which second derivatives occur. The two integrations which transform the second derivatives into the functions yield two arbitrary constants, so that we have six constants in all. For their determination we need six given values. This may be expressed physically as follows; the natural law is only concerned with the acceleration, and while a particle may have a definite acceleration, it can have any velocity or position. The fact that velocity and position are not determined but characterize the special case and therefore must be given in order to deal with this case, is expressed mathematically by the order of the differential equations. If, however, at any moment the three velocity components and the three position coordinates are given, their future development is subject to the differential equation and we can calculate their values at any instant, assuming of course that we are able to integrate the differential equation.

As an example we shall take as the "initial values" at the time $t = 0$:

$$x = 0, \qquad y = h, \qquad z = a,$$

$$\frac{dx}{dt} = 0, \qquad \frac{dy}{dt} = 0, \qquad \frac{dz}{dt} = 0. \tag{2.6}$$

This means physically that at the moment $t = 0$ a particle at the point 0, h, a, which has no initial velocity is allowed to fall under the sole influence of its weight. This is "free fall".

The three differential equations (2.5) are simultaneous, i.e., they contain three unknowns and are valid at the same time. In this case they are very simple, since each equation contains only one unknown. Since the same is true for the initial conditions, the mathematical problem is reduced to the integration of three independent differential equations of the second order, for each of which two initial conditions are given. The general solution is also elementary in our case. With the arbitrary constants $C_1 \cdots C_6$, we obtain

$$x = C_1 t + C_2 \,, \quad y = -\frac{gt^2}{2} + C_3 t + C_4 \,,$$

$$z = C_5 t + C_6 \,, \tag{2.7}$$

where $g = G/m$ is the acceleration of free fall. These equations are equivalent to the differential equations (2.5). From them we obtain the solution of the special case if we form $dx/dt \cdots$, then introduce in all expressions $t = 0$ and the corresponding values according to (2.6), and finally solve the six linear equations with respect to the six unknowns $C_1 \cdots C_6$. A problem of this kind can be very difficult to evaluate. In our case, however, it is elementary. It is sufficient to give the result:

$$x = 0, \qquad y = -\frac{gt^2}{2} + h, \qquad z = a \tag{2.8}$$

These expressions and their derivatives with respect to t give us the position and the velocity of the point at any time, and all questions concerning the trajectory can be answered numerically. Often the main task of the physicist begins here, namely the physical interpretation of the mathematical results. We can not treat this third part of the problem here, but must be satisfied with the two preliminary parts: 1. Translation of the physical problem into the mathematical form ((2.5) and (2.6)), 2. Transformation into the mathematical solution (2.8). Two other simple examples are given to illustrate the procedure.

3. Trajectory of a projectile

A particle is thrown from a height h at an angle α, and with an initial speed v_0. How does the motion develop?

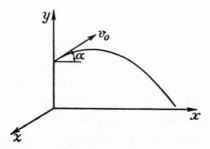

Fig. 1. Trajectory of a Projectile

The differential equations remain the same (2.5) as above. We note, incidentally, that the ratio G/m has the same value for all bodies. This value g is the "acceleration due to gravity". The vertical line through the initial position of the particle may again be chosen as y-axis, and we let the projection of the direction of the initial velocity on the horizontal plane determine the direction of the x-axis.

Then we have for the initial position $(t = 0)$.

$$x = 0, \qquad y = h, \qquad z = 0,$$

and for the initial speed,

$$\frac{dx}{dt} = v_0 \cos \alpha, \qquad \frac{dy}{dt} = v_0 \sin \alpha, \qquad \frac{dz}{dt} = 0.$$

Without regard to the initial conditions, the solution is again (2.7). By use of the initial conditions we obtain

$$x = (v_0 \cos \alpha)t,$$

$$y = -\frac{gt^2}{2} + (v_0 \sin \alpha)t + h \qquad z = 0.$$

(2.9)

The position and the velocity at any moment t follow immediately from these formulae. The same is true for the times corresponding to prescribed values of the coordinates, such as the time corresponding to $y = 0$. Furthermore, by elimination of t one obtains a relation between x and y, describing the "trajectory" of the particle; from this relation the range, altitude, and similar quantities can easily be determined. The equation $z = 0$ shows that the whole motion takes place in a plane.

4. Friction

A particle which moves along a straight line with an initial speed v_0 is subjected to a force due to friction which is proportional to the speed of the body and therefore equal to cv. How does this motion develop?

The direction of the motion may be chosen as the x-axis. We have only one differential equation. But this time it is a bit more difficult to solve. It is the following:

$$m \frac{d^2x}{dt^2} = m \frac{dv}{dt} = -cv.$$

(2.10)

In addition we have the initial conditions that at $t = 0$, $v = v_0$ and $x = 0$. We obtain the solution of the differential equation for v by the method of "separation of variables". This means that the equation is transformed in such a way that on one side there are only quantities depending on v, while those depending on t are all on the other side. Doing this and integrating we obtain

$$\frac{dv}{v} = -\frac{c}{m} dt \qquad (2.10a)$$

or

$$\ln v = -\frac{c}{m} t + \text{const} \qquad (2.10b)$$

or

$$v = C_1 e^{-ct/m}, \qquad (2.11)$$

The constant of integration C_1 is a factor here because we have written (2.10b) in exponential form. The initial condition for v gives $C_1 = v_0$. For further integration we write

$$\frac{dx}{dt} = v_0 e^{-ct/m}$$

From this it follows that

$$x = -\frac{mv_0 e^{-ct/m}}{c} + C_2$$

and from the initial condition for x,

$$0 = -\frac{mv_0}{c} + C_2 \qquad \text{or} \qquad C_2 = \frac{mv_0}{c}.$$

Thus the result is

$$x = \frac{mv_0}{c} (1 - e^{-ct/m}); \qquad (2.12)$$

Discussing this we see that the velocity never becomes zero, while the body approaches the point $x = mv_0/c$ asymptotically.

5. The motion of a planet

Our differential equation, however, is not always of such a simple type that it can be integrated by such easy methods as simple integration or separation of variables, etc. As an example we have the classical problem in the mechanics of particles— the motion of a planet under the influence of the gravitational force of the sun. If M and m are the masses of the sun and the planet respec-

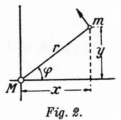

Fig. 2.

Sun and planet

tively, Newton's law of gravitation states that (with the notations of Fig. 2) $P = fMm/r^2$ (f = gravitational constant). Suppose now that we know the position and the velocity at a certain instant, and let us choose our coordinate system so that the x, y-plane contains the sun (as origin) and the direction of the planetary motion at the instant $t = 0$. Then for $t = 0$ we have $z = 0$ and $dz/dt = 0$, and we obtain the differential equations

$$\frac{d^2x}{dt^2} = -\frac{fM}{r^2} \cos \varphi = -\frac{fMx}{r^3},$$

$$\frac{d^2y}{dt^2} = -\frac{fM}{r^2} \sin \varphi = -\frac{fMy}{r^3},$$

(2.13)

while d^2z/dt^2 is proportional to z, and by the initial conditions is always equal to zero. Thus $r^2 = x^2 + y^2$, and we have two simultaneous differential equations and four initial conditions. Both contain x and y in a rather complicated manner, however, and an elementary solution is not possible. There still exist fundamental methods for a solution, which we now intend to deduce from the general equation and which we shall later apply to the special case of the planetary motion.

6. Energy

We start with the general vector equation

$$m \frac{d\mathbf{v}}{dt} = \mathbf{P} \qquad (2.14)$$

and form the scalar product of either of its sides with the vector $\mathbf{v}$. The scalar product $\mathbf{A} \cdot \mathbf{B}$ of two vectors $\mathbf{A}$ and $\mathbf{B}$ is the quantity $AB \cos \alpha$, where A and B are the lengths (magnitudes) of the two vectors Thus the scalar product is the product of the length of one of the vectors and the projection of the second vector on to the first (Fig. 3). In rectangular coordinates this is simply

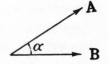

Fig. 3. Scalar product of two vectors

$$\mathbf{A} \cdot \mathbf{B} = A_x B_x + A_y B_y + A_z B_z . \qquad (2.15)$$

From the elements of differential calculus, it follows that

$$m \frac{d\mathbf{v}}{dt} \cdot \mathbf{v} = \frac{d}{dt} \left(\frac{mv^2}{2} \right).$$

Since $\mathbf{v} = d\mathbf{r}/dt$, multiplication of

$$m \frac{d\mathbf{v}}{dt} \cdot \mathbf{v} = \mathbf{P} \cdot \mathbf{v}$$

by dt gives the general equation

$$d\left(\frac{mv^2}{2}\right) = \mathbf{P} \cdot d\mathbf{r}. \qquad (2.16)$$

This equation expresses the energy theorem of mechanics; "The increment of the 'kinetic energy' $mv^2/2$ is equal to the 'work' done by the force $\mathbf{P}$ on the corresponding element $d\mathbf{r}$ of the trajectory." This equation can be integrated immediately, if $\mathbf{P}$ depends only on the position (and not on the velocity). In this case the integral $- \int \mathbf{P} \cdot d\mathbf{r}$ (which contains an arbitrary constant) is called the "potential energy" of the mass m at the point which is given by the upper limit of the integral. This potential energy is the work which must be done against the force $\mathbf{P}$ in order to move the particle from the arbitrary initial point to the point $\mathbf{r}$ under consideration. The energy theorem now appears in this simple form; "The sum of the potential and kinetic energies is constant during the entire motion".

With this integral we have derived a relation in which the time does not occur and in which there are no second derivatives, but only the first derivative $\mathbf{v} = d\mathbf{r}/dt$ appears.

In our example of the planetary motion we can obtain the same result by multiplying the first equation (2.13) by dx/dt, the second by dy/dt and adding both, corresponding to (2.15). We obtain

$$d\left[\frac{m}{2}\left\{\left(\frac{dx}{dt}\right)^2 + \left(\frac{dy}{dt}\right)^2\right\}\right] = -\frac{fMm}{r^3}(x\,dx + y\,dy). \, (2.17)$$

The expression $(dx/dt)^2 + (dy/dt)^2$ is the square of the velocity (which is formed from the two velocity components) and may be designated by v^2.

This equation is integrable. We take the values corresponding to $t = 0$ (which may be characterized by a subscript 0) as the lower limits. Then we obtain

$$\frac{m}{2}(v^2 - v_0^2)$$

$$= -fMm\left[\int_{x_0}^{x}\frac{x\,dx}{(x^2 + y^2)^{3/2}} + \int_{y_0}^{y}\frac{y\,dy}{(x^2 + y^2)^{3/2}}\right]^{1)}$$

$$= fMm\left[\frac{1}{(x^2 + y^2)^{\frac{1}{2}}} - \frac{1}{(x_0^2 + y_0^2)^{\frac{1}{2}}}\right]$$

$$= fMm\left(\frac{1}{r} - \frac{1}{r_0}\right)$$

or

$$\frac{m}{2}v^2 - f\frac{Mm}{r} = \frac{m}{2}v_0^2 - f\frac{Mm}{r_0} \qquad (2.18)$$

Thus for each position we know the magnitude of the velocity which the planet must have there, but not the direction. Also we cannot obtain any information in this way about how the point moves with time.

It is important to note that (2.18) contains only first derivatives $[v^2 = (dx/dt)^2 + (dy/dt)^2]$ and no second derivatives, and thus is only of the first order.

7. Moment of Momentum

We can find a first integral of the Newton equation with only first derivatives in a similar way to the above

---

[1] In the first integral y has the constant value y_0, and in the second x has the constant value x_0.

by multiplying the differential equation

$$m \frac{d\mathbf{v}}{dt} = \mathbf{P}$$

by **r** (vector product). The origin of the vector **r**, although arbitrary, must be fixed.

The vector product $\mathbf{A} \times \mathbf{B}$ is, so far as magnitude is concerned, the area of the parallelogram shown in Fig. 4, i.e., $AB \sin \alpha$. The orientation of this plane surface in space can be characterized by two angles. Therefore the vector-product can be determined by three numbers, similar to a vector. The simplest way to choose these numbers is to

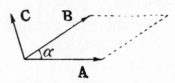

Fig. 4. The vector product of two vectors

take the areas of the projections of the parallelogram on three perpendicular planes. Since it can be determined by three numbers, the vector product can be represented by a vector. (However, it is not a vector). For this representation one takes a vector **C** perpendicular to the parallelogram and with a length numerically equal to the area of the parallelogram. Furthermore, the orientation of **C** shall be such that **A**, **B**, **C** in this order form a right-handed coordinate system. Then we have $\mathbf{A} \times \mathbf{B} = -\mathbf{B} \times \mathbf{A}$. The three rectangular components of **C** are

$$[\mathbf{A} \times \mathbf{B}]_z = \mathbf{A}_x \mathbf{B}_y - \mathbf{A}_y \mathbf{B}_x \; ;$$

$$[\mathbf{A} \times \mathbf{B}]_x = \mathbf{A}_y \mathbf{B}_z - \mathbf{A}_z \mathbf{B}_y \; ;$$

$$[\mathbf{A} \times \mathbf{B}]_y = \mathbf{A}_z \mathbf{B}_x - \mathbf{A}_x \mathbf{B}_z \; .$$

We obtain

$$m \frac{d\mathbf{v}}{dt} \times \mathbf{r} = \mathbf{P} \times \mathbf{r}. \qquad (2.19)$$

The expression on the right is called the "moment" of the force $\mathbf{P}$ with respect to the origin. Fig. 5 shows us the relation between this definition of "moment" and the usual one which uses the perpendicular from the origin to the direction of the force, for in Fig. 5 $h = r \sin \alpha$. The expression on the left-hand side can be transformed by the use of

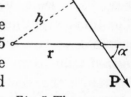

Fig. 5. The moment

$$\frac{d}{dt} (\mathbf{v} \times \mathbf{r}) = \frac{d\mathbf{v}}{dt} \times \mathbf{r} + \mathbf{v} \times \frac{d\mathbf{r}}{dt}.$$

Since $d\mathbf{r}/dt = \mathbf{v}$, and the vector product of any vector with itself is equal to 0 ($\alpha = 0$), it follows from (2.19) that

$$\frac{d}{dt} (m\mathbf{v} \times \mathbf{r}) = \mathbf{P} \times \mathbf{r}. \qquad (2.20)$$

The quantity $m\mathbf{v} \times \mathbf{r}$ is called the "moment of momentum" of the particle with respect to the origin. The derivative of the moment of momentum with respect to the time is equal to the moment of the force (for any position of the origin). This theorem can be used for integration whenever the origin can be so chosen that the moment of the force is a simple expression, for example zero. This can always be done for all "central forces". These are forces which at any position are always directed towards a fixed point. If this fixed point is used as the origin, then the moment of the force is equal to zero in the whole space. Our problem of the motion of a planet may serve as an example if the sun is taken as the origin. This can also be seen formally if in our equation (2.13) we write the vector multiplication in coordinate form. Multiplying the upper equation by y, and the lower one by x and subtracting, we find the right-hand sides will cancel out. This means physically that the moment is equal to zero. We obtain then

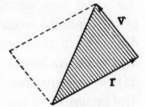

Fig. 6. The vector product as an area

$$m\left\{\frac{d^2x}{dt^2}\,y - \frac{d^2y}{dt^2}\,x\right\} = 0$$

or by a simple transformation

$$m\,\frac{d}{dt}\left\{\frac{dx}{dt}\,y - \frac{dy}{dt}\,x\right\} = 0.$$

From this we obtain for the moment of momentum

$$m\left\{\frac{dx}{dt}\,y - \frac{dy}{dt}\,x\right\} = \text{const.} \qquad (2.21)$$

Thus we again obtain an integral of the equations of motion which is only of first order. The vector product in this equation is the area of the parallelogram formed by the velocity vector and the radius vector of the sun. This is twice the area of the triangle which is covered in unit time by the moving radius vector. This is the second law of Kepler. We have thus shown this law to be a consequence of the general theorem on moments. It states "The moving radius vector sweeps equal areas in equal times".

We were able to transform the equations (2.13) into the simpler equations (2.18) and (2.21) with the aid of the two general theorems. From these we could obtain the other laws of Kepler by further integrations. These, however, are not of a general nature. They hold only for the special case and therefore we shall not consider them.

8. Systems of particles

We proceed from the problem of the mechanics of a single particle to examples with several particles. The particles are acted upon by exterior forces and by interior forces which represent the mutual influences of the particles of the system on each other. The interior forces occur only as couples of two forces, equal in magnitude but opposite in direction. Not only are the two forces $\mathbf{J}_{21}$ and $\mathbf{J}_{12}$ exerted by the point 1 on point 2 and vice versa, equal and opposite but the same is true for the moments of these forces with respect to an arbitrary point. The motion of such a system of n points can be described by n vector equations or by $3n$ equations for the components of the forces and the accelerations. They are

$$m_1 \frac{d\mathbf{v_1}}{dt} = \mathbf{P}_1 + \mathbf{J}_{12} + \mathbf{J}_{13} + \cdots + \mathbf{J}_{1n}$$

$$m_2 \frac{d\mathbf{v_2}}{dt} = \mathbf{P}_2 + \mathbf{J}_{21} + \mathbf{J}_{23} + \cdots + \mathbf{J}_{2n} \qquad (2.22)$$

$$\cdots \cdots \cdots \cdots \cdots \cdots \cdots \cdots \cdots \cdots \cdots \cdots$$

$$m_n \frac{d\mathbf{v_n}}{dt} = \mathbf{P}_n + \mathbf{J}_{n1} + \mathbf{J}_{n2} + \cdots + \mathbf{J}_{n,n-1},$$

The signification of the J_{lm} and the relations between
them follow from Fig. 7. To the exterior forces corre-

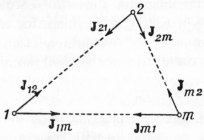

Fig. 7. Interior forces

spond opposite forces of the same strength, but since
they act on points exterior to the system we need not
consider them. The limitation of a mechanical system
in space, and consequently the distinction between
interior and exterior forces is arbitrary and suggested
by practical considerations.

In order to integrate the system (2.22) we must try
to eliminate the interior forces. The integrals without
interior forces express the main theorems of mechanics
of systems of particles.

9. Momentum theorem (motion of the center of gravity)

If we add all equations (2.22), the J_{lm} cancel one
another because they exist in couples of equal but
opposite forces. The following vector equation remains

$$\frac{d}{dt}(m_1\mathbf{v}_1 + \cdots m_n\mathbf{v}_n) = \mathbf{P}_1 + \cdots + \mathbf{P}_n .\quad (2.23)$$

The product $m_1\mathbf{v}_1$ is called the "momentum" of the
particle 1. The vector sum of all exterior forces is called

the "resultant" of the exterior forces, and the vector sum of all momenta the "total momentum" of the system. The "momentum theorem" of mechanics is contained in equation (2.23) which, for a system of particles, corresponds to Newton's equation for a single particle. "The derivative of the total momentum with respect to the time is equal in magnitude and direction to the resultant of the exterior forces." Let us introduce an ideal point having the same mass and the same momentum as the total system. This point is called the center of gravity. The same equation holds for this point as for a particle on which all the exterior forces act at the same time.

10. Moment of momentum theorem

The moments of the interior forces also exist in couples of equal but opposite moments. If then we form the vector product of the equations (2.22) with the radius vectors r_1, r_2, $\cdots$ of each point from an arbitrary point of origin and add the equations, we will again obtain a vector equation without interior forces, namely

$$m_1\left[\frac{d\mathbf{v}_1}{dt} \times \mathbf{r}_1\right] + \cdots + m_n\left[\frac{d\mathbf{v}_n}{dt} \times \mathbf{r}_n\right]$$

$$= \mathbf{P}_1 \times \mathbf{r}_1 + \cdots + \mathbf{P}_n \times \mathbf{r}_n .$$

If we use here the same transformations as in Section 7, we obtain

$$\frac{d}{dt}\left[m_1\mathbf{v}_1 \times \mathbf{r}_1 + \cdots + m_n\mathbf{v}_n \times \mathbf{r}_n\right] \qquad (2.24)$$

$$= \mathbf{P}_1 \times \mathbf{r}_1 + \cdots + \mathbf{P}_n \times \mathbf{r}_n .$$

"The derivative with respect to the time of the total moment of momentum of a system of points is equal to the resulting moment of the exterior forces". This is the "moment of momentum theorem."

The following is a simple but important special case. A rigid system of an arbitrary number of particles is allowed to rotate about a fixed axis (a system is rigid if the distance between all particles of the system is invariable). Of the three equations (2.24) only the one containing the components in the plane perpendicular to the axis is important here. Let the distance of the nth point from the axis be r_n and the angular velocity of the rotation ω. The velocity of the nth point is then $r_n\omega$. Since the velocity vector in this motion is always perpendicular to r, we have $|\mathbf{v} \times \mathbf{r}| = \omega r^2$. From (2.24) the simplified equation

$$\frac{d}{dt}\left\{\omega \sum m_n r_n^2\right\} = M,$$

follows, if M is the moment of the exterior forces with respect to the axis. The sum $\sum m_n r_n^2$ is called the moment of inertia J. The equation now becomes similar to the Newton equation (2.3a)

$$J\frac{d\omega}{dt} = M \tag{2.25}$$

If on the other hand we take the angle of rotation as a variable, the derivative with respect to the time of which is equal to the angular velocity, then

$$J\frac{d^2\varphi}{dt^2} = M. \tag{2.25a}$$

The two theorems (2.23) and (2.24) are general consequences of Newton's principles, namely of equation (2.3) for a particle, and the law that to each force there corresponds an equal and opposite reaction. The theorems therefore are generally valid.

11. Energy theorem

The integral of equation (2.22) which corresponds to our previous theorem is, however, not quite so general. If we multiply each one of the equations (2.22) by the corresponding velocity (scalar product) and add, we obtain expressions originating from the interior forces such as $J_{12} \cdot v_1 + J_{21} \cdot v_2$, etc. By projecting the vectors v_1 and v_2 on the direction of J_{12} and J_{21} we see that this sum is equal to zero if the two projections are equal and opposite, that is, if during the motion the distance of

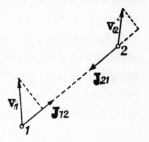

Fig. 8. Work done by the interior forces

the two points is constant. The components of v_1 and v_2 perpendicular to the line $m_1 m_2$ and the direction of this line may change. Thus we obtain an energy theorem independent of the interior forces only if the distances of the points from one another are constant, i.e. if the system is rigid. In this case we obtain the relation corresponding to (2.16) above,

$$d\left(\frac{m_1 v_1^2}{2} + \cdots + \frac{m_n v_n^2}{2}\right)$$

$$= P_1 \cdot dr_1 + \cdots + P_n \cdot dr_n .$$

(2.26)

"The increment of the total kinetic energy of a rigid mechanical system is equal to the total work of the exterior forces." If the forces are functions of the positions only, this equation is again easily integrated as in (2.16). If the system is not rigid, the work of the interior forces must be taken into consideration. Thus this theorem often becomes impractical for calculation.

Most problems of mechanics are solved with the aid of one or several of the three theorems mentioned. In certain cases they simplify (e.g., for rigid bodies, for pure rotation, etc.). It is not feasible to consider further examples here, since we would not gain any further experience concerning the construction and integration of differential equations, but only learn more about physical questions. One problem, however, is an exception, since a more direct approach gives us the solution and since it is probably the most important one in practice—the theory of oscillations.

12. Equation of oscillation

Oscillations originate wherever there is an exterior force tending to bring a displaced system back to its equilibrium position. The most simple ("harmonic") form of oscillation occurs if the intensity of the restoring force is proportional to the distance from the equilibrium position.

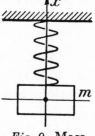

Fig. 9. Mass attached to a spring

We shall consider first a particle (Fig. 9), which is able to move along the x-axis and which is being pulled back to its equilibrium position $x = 0$ by a weightless spring such that the restoring force is $P_x = -cx$. The motion is then characterized by the differential equation

$$m \frac{d^2x}{dt^2} = -cx. \tag{2.27}$$

For the exact determination of a single case we again require two given values of initial position and velocity. If, for example, at the beginning the particle is displaced from the equilibrium position and then released without any initial velocity, we have for $t = 0$, $x = x_0$ and $dx/dt = 0$. If on the other hand the particle at its equilibrium position receives a blow at the time $t = 0$, we have at this instant: $x = 0$, $dx/dt = v_0$. In this example it is possible to find the essential properties of the motion from the differential equation alone without the aid of the initial conditions.

The differential equation (2.27) is homogeneous and linear, that is, the unknown x or one of its derivatives is contained in the same power (the first) in every term. Differential equations of this type can be integrated directly (for any order and any number of unknowns) by using exponential functions. A solution of a differential equation of this type is given by

$$x = Ae^{\alpha t}, \tag{2.28}$$

Here A is an arbitrary constant of integration, whereas the constant α can be determined from the differential equation. Since the differential equation is homogeneous and linear, an arbitrary number of such solutions may be added and the sum is again a solution. The order of the equation determines the number of independent solutions, and the necessary number of constants of integration (in our case two). We also can determine all the α's. For by introducing (2.28) in (2.27) we obtain

$$m\alpha^2 A e^\alpha = - c A e^{\alpha t},$$

and this is an algebraic equation for α since we can divide both sides by the exponential factor. The degree of the algebraic equation is determined by the order of the differential equation, and we thus obtain just the necessary number of solutions. We have in our case

$$\alpha = \pm i \left(\frac{c}{m}\right)^{\frac{1}{2}}$$

and it follows that

$$x = A e^{i(c/m)^{1/2}t} + B e^{-i(c/m)^{1/2}t}. \tag{2.29}$$

Using the well known formula

$$e^{\pm iy} = \cos y \pm i \sin y \tag{2.30}$$

we can write (2.29) in the form

$$x = (A + B) \cos \left(\frac{c}{m}\right)^{\frac{1}{2}} t + i(A - B) \sin \left(\frac{c}{m}\right)^{\frac{1}{2}} t$$

$$\tag{2.31}$$

$$= C \cos \left(\frac{c}{m}\right)^{\frac{1}{2}} t + D \sin \left(\frac{c}{m}\right)^{\frac{1}{2}} t,$$

Since the solution of the problem must be real, C and D are two real constants which can easily be determined from the initial conditions.

The trigonometric functions represent oscillations. The "frequency" of these oscillations (number of oscillations in 2π units of time) is $\nu = (c/m)^{\frac{1}{2}}$, and the "period" is $T = 2\pi(m/c)^{\frac{1}{2}}$. Both results are independent of the initial conditions and the constants of integration. On the other hand the amplitude A and phase constant φ (Fig. 10) are determined solely by the initial

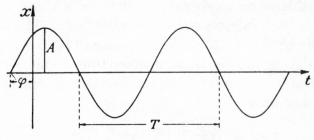

Fig. 10. Oscillation

conditions. In the majority of problems of oscillation theory the most important thing to know is the frequency, so that the initial conditions are not very important. We now generalize the problem in three ways.

13. Damped Oscillations

We assume that in addition to the restoring force which pulls the particle back to the equilibrium position there is also a force acting due to friction. This resisting force may be proportional to the speed dx/dt (factor k). This, however, is not always the exact form of a resisting force, but in most cases can be used as an approximation. The differential equation is now the following

$$m \frac{d^2x}{dt^2} = - cx - k \frac{dx}{dt} \qquad (2.32)$$

This is again homogeneous and linear and integrable in the form $x = Ae^{\alpha t}$.

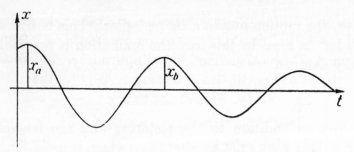

Fig. 11. Damped oscillation

We now have

$$ma^2 + ka + c = 0$$

and

$$\alpha = -\frac{k}{2m} \pm i \left(\frac{c}{m} - \frac{k^2}{4m^2} \right)^{\frac{1}{2}}. \qquad (2.33)$$

Using (2.30) again we obtain solutions of the form

$$e^{-kt/2m} \times \frac{\cos}{\sin} \left[\left(\frac{c}{m} - \frac{k^2}{4m^2} \right)^{\frac{1}{2}} t \right].$$

These are damped oscillations of "frequency"

$$\left(\frac{c}{m} - \frac{k^2}{4m^2} \right)^{\frac{1}{2}}$$

and the logarithmic decrement $k/2m$. The latter term means that the values of x which correspond to the instants t and $t + T$ (the values, for example, marked x_a and x_b in Fig. 11) have the ratio $e^{-kT/2m}$, so that the ratio of their logarithms is equal to $kT/2m$.

The influence of the damping constant on the frequency is small when the restoring force is much larger than the frictional force. If the friction is great, however, the motion may not be periodical. This is true if $k^2/4m^2 > c/m$. In this case the oscillation is aperiodically damped.

14. Forced oscillation

Now in addition to the restoring and the friction force there may exist another force which is not a function of x but of the time t. For example, an exterior force tending to move the particle. We designate it by $P(t)$. The equation governing the motion is now

$$m \frac{d^2x}{dt^2} = - cx - k \frac{dx}{dt} + P(t) \qquad (2.34)$$

and is no longer homogeneous. It represents a "forced" and not a "free" oscillation. In order to find its general solution we first look for any special function $x_1(t)$ which satisfies the equation (2.34). This is only a particular solution and does not contain any constant of integration. If we add the general solution $x_2(t)$ of the homogeneous equation

$$m \frac{d^2x_2}{dt^2} = - cx_2 - k \frac{dx_2}{dt},$$

which we already know, then the sum $x_1 + x_2$ is also a solution of (2.34), and moreover it is the complete one. In our case the particular solution x_1 is often called the "forced oscillation" while x_2 is called "free oscillation". The latter is superposed on the former in a way which is determined by the initial conditions. The remaining task, to find a particular solution, is solved by the so called method of "variation of parameters", and it is assumed that the reader is familiar with this method from elementary courses.

We shall restrict our considerations to the case where the exterior force is periodical. This case is the most important one in practice and can be handled easily. The differential equation is

$$m \frac{d^2x}{dt^2} + k \frac{dx}{dt} + cx = P_0 \cos \omega t, \qquad (2.35)$$

where P_0 is the amplitude, and ω the frequency of the exterior force. We want to know the amplitude, the frequency, and the phase of the forced oscillation x_1 which is any particular solution without a constant of integration. If k were equal to 0, we could use a function proportional to $\cos \omega t$ for x_1. For then each term would contain the factor $\cos \omega t$, which consequently would cancel out. Since k is different from zero, x_1 will be more complicated. There will be a difference of phase between the force and the oscillation. The most convenient practical method to find a particular solution of (2.35) is the following. By the addition of $iP_0 \sin \omega t$, the right hand term of the equation becomes equal to $P_0 e^{i\omega t}$. The solution of the complex equation

$$m \frac{d^2x_1}{dt^2} + k \frac{dx_1}{dt} + cx_1 = P_0 e^{i\omega t} \qquad (2.36)$$

is now a complex function x_1, the real part of which is the solution of (2.35) we are looking for, while we are not interested in the imaginary part. This transition from trigonometric functions to complex exponential functions is often used to simplify the integration of differential equations. If in (2.36) we put $x_1 = Ae^{i\omega t}$, the factor $e^{i\omega t}$ cancels out in all terms and the remaining equation is

$$A(-m\omega^2 + ik\omega + c) = P_0$$

or

$$A = \frac{P_0}{-m\omega^2 + c + ik\omega} = \frac{P_0(-m\omega^2 + c - ik\omega)}{(-m\omega^2 + c)^2 + k^2\omega^2}.$$

We shall write A in the form $A = Ce^{i\varphi}$, where

$$C = \frac{P_0}{(c - m\omega^2)^2 + k^2\omega^2} \quad \text{and} \quad \tan\varphi = \frac{k}{m\omega^2 - c}.$$

Then our particular solution of (2.35) is

$$x_1 = \text{real part of } [Ce^{i(\omega t - \varphi)}] = C\cos(\omega t + \varphi), \quad (2.37)$$

From this we immediately obtain the amplitude and the difference of phase between the forced oscillation and the exterior force. The most important result of (2.37) is the possibility of "resonance", that is large amplitudes in the solution if k is small and $\omega = (c/m)^{\frac{1}{2}}$, the frequency of the free oscillation.[1]

15. Coupled oscillations

Two or more oscillating systems can be coupled. We shall demonstrate the setting up and the integration of

[1] The determination of the free oscillation has been given in Section 13.

the corresponding differential equations for the most simple example of two particles, the first of which is pulled into a certain position of equilibrium by a spring (as above), while the other particle is connected with the first one by yet another spring. We assume no friction or exterior forces. We designate the displacements of the two particles from their respective equilibrium positions by x and y. The force exerted on the first particle by the first spring is of the form c_1x, while the second spring acts

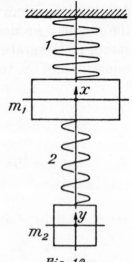

Fig. 12.
Coupled oscillations

on the second particle with a force $c_2(y - x)$, as the extension of the second spring is given by the difference of x and y. The differential equations are now

$$m_1 \frac{d^2x}{dt^2} = -c_1x + c_2(y - x) = -(c_1 + c_2)x + c_2y,$$

$$(2.38)$$

$$m_2 \frac{d^2y}{dt^2} = -c_2(y - x).$$

These are again two simultaneous and homogeneous equations. Equations of this kind can be reduced to a single equation by elimination of one of the unknowns. We can, for example, solve the second equation in (2.38) with respect to x and then introduce the expression for x so obtained into the first equation. Then we will have an equation of fourth order which can be integrated by the method we used previously. There are four constants of integration corresponding to the two initial positions and the two initial velocities of the two points. However we are particularly interested in the consequences of the differential equations themselves.

We can also apply the method of exponential functions without the above-mentioned elimination, and this is usually the simpler way. We try the following expressions

$$x = A_1 e^{at}, \qquad y = A_2 e^{at} \qquad (2.39)$$

and obtain from (2.38) the expressions

$$A_1(m_1\alpha^2 + c_1 + c_2) - A_2 c_2 = 0,$$
$$(2.40)$$
$$-A_1 c_2 + A_2(m_2\alpha^2 + c_2) = 0.$$

These are two homogeneous linear algebraic equations for A_1 and A_2. Whenever the equations are independent of one another, the only solution is $A_1 = A_2 = 0$. If the equations are dependent on one another, they only determine the ratio A_2/A_1 while the absolute values of the unknowns are still undetermined. This corresponds to the free choice of one integration constant. Since for $A_1 = A_2 = 0$ we would have $x = y = 0$, the latter case (the two equations dependent) is the one which actually occurs. That means that the determinant of the system of equations is equal to zero, which for our example means that

$$\begin{vmatrix} m_1\alpha^2 + c_1 + c_2 & -c_2 \\ -c_2 & m_2\alpha^2 + c_2 \end{vmatrix} = 0. \quad (2.41)$$

This relation can also be obtained by direct calculation of A_2/A_1 from both equations. However, to set the determination equal to zero is more convenient when there are more than two unknowns.

Equation (2.41)

$$(m_1\alpha^2 + c_1 + c_2)(m_2\alpha^2 + c_2) - c_2^2 = 0$$

gives us two values for α^2 corresponding to the two frequencies. To each frequency there corresponds an amplitude and a phase constant. But for the term $-c_2^2$ on the left-hand side, the two frequencies furnished by this equation would equal the frequencies of the masses m_1 and m_2 on the springs c_1 and $c_1 + c_2$, respectively. The quantity c_2 is thus characteristic for the coupling by spring 2. The two afore-mentioned frequencies are changed by the coupling. In acoustics this is called "being out of tune". The equation for the frequencies in the general case is of a higher degree, and usually not of the second degree for α^2 as in our example.

16. Coupling by friction

The coupling also can be obtained by friction or similar forces. A simple mechanical example is the following one. Two disks are restored to the equilibrium position by springs which permit rotational oscillations (Fig. 13). Between the two disks there may be a small amount of a viscous liquid, the frictional force

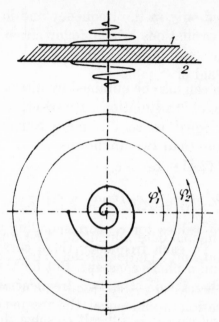

Fig. 13. Rotational oscillations coupled by friction

of which is proportional to the relative angular velocity of the disks. This example has technical significance in connection with the performance of anti-rolling tanks in ships.

The differential equations are, according to (2.32),

$$J_1 \frac{d^2\varphi_1}{dt^2} = -c_1\varphi_1 - k\left(\frac{d\varphi_1}{dt} - \frac{d\varphi_2}{dt}\right),$$

$$J_2 \frac{d^2\varphi_2}{dt^2} = -c_2\varphi_2 - k\left(\frac{d\varphi_2}{dt} - \frac{d\varphi_1}{dt}\right), \tag{2.42}$$

where φ_1 and φ_2 are the angular displacements of the disks, and J_1 and J_2 are the moments of inertia. Since we are interested only in the frequency and in the damping of the oscillations which follow from (2.42), we do not require any initial conditions.

With the aid of

$$\varphi_1 = A_1 e^{\alpha t}, \qquad \varphi_2 = A_2 e^{\alpha t},$$

we obtain

$$A_1(J_1\alpha^2 + k\alpha + c_1) + A_2(-k\alpha) = 0,$$

$$A_1(-k\alpha) + A_2(J_2\alpha^2 + k\alpha + c_2) = 0.$$

Since the principal determinant must be equal to 0, we have the following equation of the fourth degree for α:

$$(J_1\alpha^2 + k\alpha + c_1)(J_2\alpha^2 + k\alpha + c_2) - k^2\alpha^2 = 0. \quad (2.43)$$

In the general case it is difficult to solve this equation which gives us four (complex) values for α. Since this solution constitutes a different problem in each case, we are not able to say anything general about it. Each of the complex values of α represents an oscillation, the frequency of which is given by the imaginary part of α, while the damping is given by the real part [compare (2.33)]. Since the four solutions form two couples of conjugate imaginary numbers, we only have two values for the frequency. Two or four of the solutions can be real. The corresponding oscillation is not periodic in this case.

17. Stability

The problem of stability is another one of the many cases in which the equations of motion of a mechanical system are homogeneous and linear differential equations. If a system is in stationary equilibrium (for example a rigid body (airplane) in a motion that does not change with time), this motion satisfies as many conditions of equilibrium as there are degrees of freedom. A rigid body for example, can move in three directions and rotate about three axes. It has six degrees of freedom. Its stationary motion satisfies the six conditions of equilibrium which express the balance between forces and moments. We now assume that the equilibrium is slightly disturbed so that one or several variables of the motion have values different from those in the equilibrium. We shall assume in addition that the disturbance is so small that all forces and moments can be represented as linear functions of the disturbances (in the same way as a curve in a small neighbourhood of a point can be represented by the tangent). As a consequence of the disturbance, the motion is now accelerated; the equilibrium is disturbed. The linear and angular accelerations also are linear functions of the variables which describe the disturbance, and so the differential equations are linear in these variables. The differential equations are also homogeneous, for the components of the forces and moments which are free from disturbance correspond to the equilibrium condition and therefore cancel one another. Thus problems of stability are described by equations of the same type as the equation of oscillation, and therefore can be solved by using exponential functions $Ae^{\alpha t}$. This method is called "method of small oscillations", although in special cases the result may not be periodical.

For α we obtain as many values as correspond to the number and the orders of the differential equations. If the real parts of all quantities α are negative, all oscillations are decreasing as the time proceeds, and this happens the faster the greater the absolute values of these negative quantities α are. The original motion is stable in this case. If, on the other hand, one or several of the quantities α have a positive real part, then the disturbance increases. The original motion will not be restored and is instable. Any problem of stability can be solved on this basis. Nevertheless the numerical diffculties can be very great particularly for the determination of the quantities α as solutions of an algebraic equation of a higher degree.

CHAPTER III

THE SIMPLEST PARTIAL DIFFERENTIAL EXPRESSIONS

1. Gradient

In all field equations, the unknowns (which are scalars, vectors, or tensors) depend on the time and on the three space coordinates. It is clear that in equations describing physical reality, the derivatives can not be contained in arbitrary combinations. Thus only those expressions which have a meaning independent of the coordinate system can appear in equations of this kind. The coordinate system is arbitrarily chosen and has as little meaning for the natural phenomena which are described by the differential equations as has the frame of the glasses for the house which we see through them. If, for example, u is a scalar and x a space coordinate, then $\partial u/\partial x$ by itself cannot have a physical meaning. Since the coordinate system is arbitrary, what at one instant is the x-axis can at some other instant be the y-axis. Similarly the vector $\mathbf{P}$ appeared in the differential equations which we have already encountered, but never the component P_x alone. The component only appeared in component equations together with the corresponding equations for the other components.

Our task is to find differential expressions which have a physical meaning and, being independent of the coordinate system, are defined in any system. The first expression of this kind corresponds to the derivative itself and describes the variations of a scalar field at a certain point (x, y, z) of space. This variation is evidently not a scalar as in the case of differentiation with respect to the time. It is different in different directions. There exist, however, relations between the derivatives in different directions. We assume the concepts of partial and total derivatives to be known. Let us start from the point (x, y, z) and move along the vector $d\mathbf{r}$, which

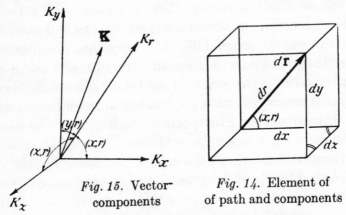

Fig. 15. Vector-components

Fig. 14. Element of of path and components

may have the length dr and the components dx, dy, dz (Fig. 14). Then if Φ is any scalar function, we have

$$\frac{\partial \Phi}{\partial r} dr = \frac{\partial \Phi}{\partial x} dx + \frac{\partial \Phi}{\partial y} dy + \frac{\partial \Phi}{\partial z} dz$$

or   (3.1)

$$\frac{\partial \Phi}{\partial r} = \frac{\partial \Phi}{\partial x} \cos(x, r) + \frac{\partial \Phi}{\partial y} \cos(y, r) + \frac{\partial \Phi}{\partial z} \cos(z, r).$$

Thus the derivative in any direction can be expressed by the three quantities $\partial \Phi / \partial x$, $\partial \Phi / \partial y$, $\partial \Phi / \partial z$, and this expression has the same form as the expression of a component K_r of a vector $\mathbf{K}$ by means of three perpendicular components K_x, K_v, K_z. The direction of the vector $\mathbf{K}$

is the direction for which the component in this direction has a maximum absolute attainable value. This length is equal to the Pythagoric sum of the three components. In the same way we can easily calculate (we assume this to be known) that in a certain direction r_0, $\partial\Phi/\partial r$ has a maximum value and is equal to zero in all directions perpendicular to this. In the direction opposite to r_0, we have a minimum of the same absolute value as the maximum. Thus a vector in the three-dimensional space corresponds to the derivative in the case of one variable. This vector corresponds in length and in direction to the maximum rate of increase of the scalar Φ from the point under consideration. Its component in any direction is equal to the partial derivative in this direction. This vector is called the "gradient" (grad).

The vector grad Φ has the components $\partial\Phi/\partial x$, $\partial\Phi/\partial y$, $\partial\Phi/\partial z$ and in general the component $\partial\Phi/\partial r$ in the direction r.

$$| \text{grad } \Phi | = \left(\left(\frac{\partial\Phi}{\partial x}\right)^2 + \left(\frac{\partial\Phi}{\partial y}\right)^2 + \left(\frac{\partial\Phi}{\partial z}\right)^2\right)^{\frac{1}{2}}. \quad (3.2)$$

The variation of a scalar with respect to the space coordinates can be contained in any physical equation in the form of the vector grad (or ∇, pronounced "del") only. As an example, we may choose a heat flow q which is proportional to grad T everywhere (T = temperature). If T is a function of position, then grad T is the vector which gives the increment of T in every direction and at every point. The heat flows in the direction opposite to the gradient (from higher to lower temperature). The factor of proportionality, λ, is called the conductivity of the material. The equation is

$$\mathbf{q} = -\lambda \operatorname{grad} T. \qquad (3.3)$$

For any direction there is a certain heat flow; the greatest flow is in the direction opposite to grad T. No heat flows in the directions perpendicular to grad T, for which T is constant.

2. Cylindrical and spherical coordinates

The vector grad Φ has a significance independent of the coordinate system. It represents the properties of variation of the scalar Φ at a certain point. All we have to do to find the component of this vector in any direction is to take two points in this direction and to divide the corresponding difference of Φ by the distance between the points. We may use any coordinate system

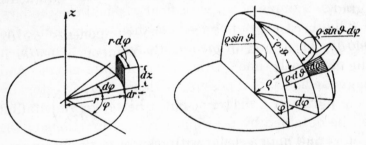

Fig. 16. Cylindrical and spherical coordinates

for this purpose. Consider, for example, cylindrical coordinates. In this system, the elements of length are

$$dr, \qquad r\,d\varphi, \qquad dz.$$

The corresponding components of the gradient are

$$\frac{\partial \Phi}{\partial r}, \qquad \frac{1}{r}\frac{\partial \Phi}{\partial \varphi}, \qquad \frac{\partial \Phi}{\partial z}. \qquad (3.4)$$

In spherical coordinates, the length elements are

$$d\rho, \qquad \rho\, d\vartheta, \qquad \rho \sin \vartheta\, d\varphi,$$

and the components of the gradient

$$\frac{\partial \Phi}{\partial \rho}, \qquad \frac{1}{\rho}\frac{\partial \Phi}{\partial \vartheta}, \qquad \frac{1}{\rho \sin \vartheta}\frac{\partial \Phi}{\partial \varphi}. \tag{3.5}$$

3. Vector fields

Besides scalar fields, there exist vector fields defined by a vector (e.g. q) which is variable in the space. Such a vector is not always the gradient of a scalar field, as in the case of the heat flow q. The condition under which a vector field is a gradient field will be established below [(3.23)].

As an example of a vector field we shall use the flow of a fluid. At every point where there is any fluid, the velocity has a certain magnitude and direction (which can vary with time). Other examples are electric and magnetic fields. It is possible to denote these vectors by some points in a diagram, but a better representation can be obtained by drawing only the directions of the vectors and not the lengths. In this case we obtain continuous lines which at every point have the direction of the vector to be represented. Best known of all are the lines in a magnetic field, which can be seen as the pattern formed by iron filing placed in the magnetic field. They are called "lines of force" in this case. The corresponding lines in a fluid are called "streamlines". Any section of the field whose surface is composed of lines of force or streamlines is called a tube of force or a stream tube. The component of the field vector in the direction perpendicular to the surface of such a tube is always equal to zero.

4. Divergence

Assume now a vector field in which there is a closed surface dividing the space into two parts—the interior and the exterior of the surface. For each element of this surface, the product "element of surface df times the normal component of the field vector (exterior normal)" has a value which is independent of the coordinate system. It can be represented by the scalar product of the field vector with another vector whose length is equal to the area of the element and the direction of which is that of the direction of the exterior normal to the element. The integral of this

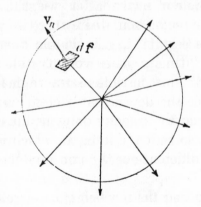

Fig. 17. Source, element of an arbitrary surface

product over the whole closed surface has a physical significance. If the field vector is the velocity of a fluid flow, then the product is the volume of liquid which flows through the element from the interior to the exterior in unit time. Thus the integral represents the volume of fluid leaving the interior. At points on the surface where **v** is directed into the interior the integrand becomes negative, of course. The integral thus represents the total strength of all sources in the interior. If the latter is not equal to zero, this can be caused either by streamlines originating in the interior or by streamlines along which the flow rate increases or decreases. In the hydrodynamical example, the first case corresponds to a flow with a source in the interior (Fig. 17), while the second case corresponds to the stationary flow of a gas

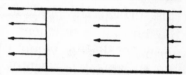

Fig. 18. Flow with variable density

in which the density decreases in the direction of the flow (Fig. 18). For, in the latter case, the same mass of gas enters the region bounded by the two walls and two cross sections (Fig. 18) in unit time as it leaves it. Thus the product "density times velocity times area of entrance or exit" must have the same value for both cross sections. Since the density is different on the two sections, the products "velocity times area of cross section" are different, so that the integral, which in this case is equal to the difference of the two products, is different from zero.

In order to find the mathematical expression for the "magnitude of a source" at a point in space, we have to take a closed surface which contains an infinitely small neighbourhood of this point. In this way the integral becomes infinitesimal of third order (the surface itself is of second order, but the difference between the field vector at the point of entrance and point of exit also becomes infinitesimal). Thus if we divide by the volume

V of the enclosed region, we shall have a finite limit. We call this limit the "divergence" (div) of the field,

$$\text{div } \mathbf{A} = \lim_{V \to 0} \frac{1}{V} \int \mathbf{A}_n \, df. \qquad (3.6)$$

The divergence is a scalar.

5. Mathematical expression of the divergence

The calculation of the divergence in various coordinate systems is now simple. In rectangular systems we use an infinitesimal cube in the field. $\mathbf{A}$, the edges of

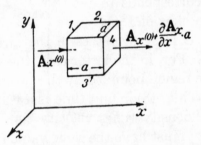

Fig. 19. Derivation of the formula for the divergence

which are of length a parallel to the axes of the system. In this case the normal components of the vector on the surface elements of the cube are either A_x or A_y or A_z. The positive direction is the one which points perpendicularly into the interior for the planes 1, 2, 3, and to the exterior for the other planes. Therefore we have $A_n = -A_x$ on 1 and $A_n = A_x$ on 4. The integral taken over 1 is equal to $-A_{x0} \cdot a^2$ if A_{x0} is the average of A_x on 1. The difference between A_x on 4 and A_x on 1 is so small that we can assume linear dependence. For constant y and z we then have

$$\mathbf{A}_x(a) = \mathbf{A}_x(0) + \frac{\partial \mathbf{A}_x}{\partial x} a$$

and the value of the integral over 4 is

$$\left\{ \mathbf{A}_{x0} + \left(\frac{\partial \mathbf{A}_x}{\partial x} \right)_0 a \right\} a^2,$$

if $(\partial \mathbf{A}_x / \partial x)_0$ is the average value of the derivative over 1. The same consideration is valid for the other planes. Since the average values go over into the values themselves in the limiting process when $a \to 0$, we obtain

$$\text{div } \mathbf{A} = \lim_{a \to 0} \frac{1}{a^3} \int \mathbf{A}_n \, df$$

$$= \lim_{a \to 0} \frac{1}{a^3} \left[\mathbf{A}_x + \frac{\partial \mathbf{A}_x}{\partial x} a - \mathbf{A}_x + \mathbf{A}_y \right.$$

$$\left. + \frac{\partial \mathbf{A}_y}{\partial y} a - \mathbf{A}_y + \mathbf{A}_z + \frac{\partial \mathbf{A}_z}{\partial z} a - \mathbf{A}_z \right] a^2,$$

$$\text{div } \mathbf{A} = \frac{\partial \mathbf{A}_x}{\partial x} + \frac{\partial \mathbf{A}_y}{\partial y} + \frac{\partial \mathbf{A}_z}{\partial z}. \tag{3.7}$$

Similar calculations are easy for any other coordinate system if one constructs the volume element with the elements of coordinates. Fig. 20 shows an element in

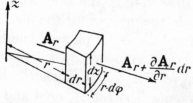

Fig. 20. Calculation of the divergence in cylindrical coordinates

(Note: dr, dz, $d\varphi$ in Fig. 20 should be replaced by Δr, Δz, $\Delta \varphi$)

cylindrical coordinates. The difference here is that the three coordinates are not equivalent. The finite but small dimensions of the element may be Δr, $r\Delta\varphi$ and Δz. The integral over the different parts of the surfaces are again (if $\mathbf{A}_r$ etc. again are the averages)

1) $-\mathbf{A}_r r\Delta\varphi\Delta z$ 4) $\left(\mathbf{A}_r + \dfrac{\partial \mathbf{A}_r}{\partial r}\,\Delta r\right)(r + \Delta r)\Delta\varphi\Delta z$

2) $-\mathbf{A}_\varphi \Delta r\Delta z$ 5) $\left(\mathbf{A}_\varphi + \dfrac{\partial \mathbf{A}_\varphi}{\partial_\varphi}\,\Delta\varphi\right)\Delta r\Delta z$

3) $-\mathbf{A}_z r\Delta r\Delta\varphi$ 6) $\left(\mathbf{A}_z + \dfrac{\partial \mathbf{A}_z}{\partial z}\,\Delta z\right)r\Delta r\Delta\varphi.$

The volume element is $r\Delta r\Delta\varphi\Delta z$. By addition and the proper limiting process we obtain

$$\text{div } \mathbf{A} = \frac{\partial \mathbf{A}_r}{\partial r} + \frac{\mathbf{A}_r}{r} + \frac{1}{r}\frac{\partial \mathbf{A}_\varphi}{\partial\varphi} + \frac{\partial \mathbf{A}_z}{\partial z}$$

$$\tag{3.8}$$

$$= \frac{1}{r}\frac{\partial}{\partial r}(r\mathbf{A}_r) + \frac{1}{r}\frac{\partial \mathbf{A}_\varphi}{\partial\varphi} + \frac{\partial \mathbf{A}_z}{\partial z}.$$

In a similar way we obtain for spherical coordinates

$$\text{div } \mathbf{A} = \frac{\partial \mathbf{A}_\rho}{\partial\rho} + \frac{2\mathbf{A}_\rho}{\rho} + \frac{1}{\rho}\frac{\partial \mathbf{A}_\vartheta}{\partial\vartheta} + \frac{\cot\vartheta}{\rho}\mathbf{A}_\vartheta$$

$$+ \frac{1}{\rho\sin\vartheta}\frac{\partial \mathbf{A}_\varphi}{\partial\varphi}$$

$$\tag{3.9}$$

$$= \frac{1}{\rho^2}\frac{\partial}{\partial\rho}(\rho^2\mathbf{A}_\rho) + \frac{1}{\rho\sin\vartheta}\frac{\partial}{\partial\vartheta}(\mathbf{A}_\vartheta\sin\vartheta)$$

$$\frac{1}{\rho\sin\vartheta}\frac{\partial \mathbf{A}_\varphi}{\partial\varphi}.$$

6. Examples and the theorem of Gauss

As an illustration of the application of the divergence in a physical example we shall use the electric and magnetic fields. The first one originates from charges only, the charges being its sources. The relation between the density of charge ρ and field $\mathbf{E}$ is

$$\text{div } \mathbf{E} = \rho. \tag{3.10}$$

On the other hand, there exist no magnetic charges, so that there are no sources, positive or negative, in the magnetic field $\mathbf{H}$. We have here

$$\text{div } \mathbf{H} = 0. \tag{3.11}$$

Let us now form the integral $\int \text{div } \mathbf{A} \, dV$ over a finite region. This region can be divided into an infinite number of infinitesimal parts, for each of which the surface integrals can be evaluated

Fig. 21. Derivation of the theorem of Gauss

as above. Each surface element which is in the interior of the original region appears in two integrals (of the two adjoining parts), and $\mathbf{A}_n$ has opposite signs in these two cases. Those integrals therefore cancel out one another and we obtain the "theorem of Gauss"

$$\int \text{div } \mathbf{A} \, dV = \int \mathbf{A}_n \, df. \tag{3.12}$$

Here the first integral is to be taken over the interior, and the second one over the surface of the region.

7. Curl

Let C be a closed plane curve in the vector field. Along this curve we shall form the integral of the scalar product of the field vector and the element $d\mathbf{s}$ of the curve. Naturally we have to determine (arbitrarily) the direction in which we shall integrate along the curve. This integral is independent of the coordinate system. If $\mathbf{A}_s$ is the vector component in

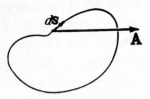

Fig. 22. Line element and vector

the direction of the tangent to the curve and ds the length of $d\mathbf{s}$, of an element of the curve, the value of the integral is $\int \mathbf{A}_s \, ds$. If the curve is now subjected to a limiting process where its length tends to 0, the value of the integral becomes small of the second order. For on one hand the length of the curve becomes small, and on the other hand the differences of the field vector on different parts of the curve are small. Dividing the integral by the area f of the plane surface enclosed by the curve, we shall therefore obtain a finite limit. This limit is called the "curl" of the vector $\mathbf{A}$:

$$\operatorname{curl} \mathbf{A} = \lim_{f \to 0} \frac{1}{f} \int \mathbf{A}_s \, ds. \qquad (3.13)$$

Now let us take any surface (not necessarily plane) which is limited by a finite curve C, and let us divide this surface into small parts, which can be considered as plane. For each one of these parts we shall form the integral as discussed above. If we add all these integrals, those parts which correspond to arcs of curves in the interior of the surface cancel out one another. Only the integral over C remains and we obtain

$$\int \text{curl } \mathbf{A} \, df = \int \mathbf{A}_s \, ds, \qquad (3.14)$$

since the line integral around any one of the infinitesimal parts is equal to curl $\mathbf{A} \, df$ corresponding to (3.13). This is the "theorem of Stokes". The nature of the curl is determined by the orientation of a plane in space, thus the curl can not be a scalar. A simple consideration shows that the values corresponding to different orientations of the curve are determined by three numbers. We shall take a triangle (Fig. 24) which may have an

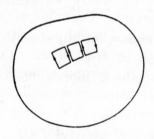

Fig. 23. Derivation of the theorem of Stokes

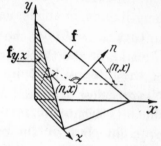

Fig. 24. Geometrical representation of the curl

arbitrary orientation in a x, y, z system as a surface element. The areas of its projections on the three coordinate-planes are $f_{yz} = f \cos (n, x) \cdots$, where n is the normal to the plane of the triangle. For infinitesimal dimensions, we have:

$f \cdot \text{curl}_{\text{triangle}} \mathbf{A} = \int \mathbf{A}_s \, ds$ over the three sides of the triangle,

$f_{yz} \cdot \text{curl}_{yz} \mathbf{A} = \int \mathbf{A}_s \, ds$ over one side of the triangle and two axes.

If we form $f_{zx} \operatorname{curl}_{zx} \mathbf{A}$ and $f_{xy} \operatorname{curl}_{xy} \mathbf{A}$ in the same way and add the three expressions together, we have taken every side of the triangle once, while the axes occur twice each and in opposite directions. Thus we have

$$f \operatorname{curl}_{\text{triangle}} \mathbf{A} = f_{xy} \operatorname{curl}_{xy} \mathbf{A}$$
$$+ f_{yz} \operatorname{curl}_{yz} \mathbf{A} + f_{zx} \operatorname{curl}_{zx} \mathbf{A}$$

or

$$\operatorname{curl}_{\text{triangle}} \mathbf{A} = (\operatorname{curl}_{xy} \mathbf{A}) \cos(nz) + (\operatorname{curl}_{yz} \mathbf{A}) \cos(nx)$$
$$+ (\operatorname{curl}_{zx} \mathbf{A}) \cos(ny). \tag{3.15}$$

so that the value of the curl is known for any direction if we know the three components of $\operatorname{curl}_{xy} \mathbf{A} \cdots$. The curl is determined by three values, like a vector.

Nevertheless the curl is not a vector since its orientation in space is not given by a line but by the orientation of a plane. It can, however, be represented by a vector, the length of which is equal to the absolute value of the curl, and the direction of which is normal to the plane of rotation. For this purpose we require a relation between the vector and the direction of rotation. Usually one uses the first three fingers of the right hand, keeping them perpendicular to one another like the axes of

Fig. 25. Correspondence between the direction of a vector and the direction of rotation in a plane

a coordinate system. Then the definition that the vector in the direction of the first finger corresponds to a rotation from the second to the third finger is used. Henceforth, we shall write curl$_z$ **A** not curl$_{xy}$ **A** as in (3.15). Equation (3.15) then becomes identical in form with (3.1) which is valid for the calculation of vector components.

8. Physical significance of the curl

To illustrate the physical significance of the curl let us consider a rotating rigid circular disk of radius r. We shall form the integral $\int$ **v**$_s$ ds along the edge of the disk. The velocity **v** has the tangential direction and its absolute value is ωr, where ω is the angular velocity. Thus the integral is equal to $\omega r 2r\pi$ and the expression $f^{-1} \int$ **v**$_s$ ds which corresponds to the curl is equal to 2ω. This means that the angular velocity is of the same nature as a curl. For another interpretation of the curl we can use the example of the mechanical work done in moving a particle along a closed curve. If **A** is a field of force, $\int$ **A**$_s$ ds is the work which the force does if the point upon which the force is acting moves along the curve. This definition is particularly useful for explaining the relation between electric current and magnetic field. We must keep in mind that this work depends on the orientation of the curve. The vector character appears only in this dependence on the orientation; the work itself is a scalar.

9. Mathematical expression of the curl

We shall first calculate the curl in rectangular coordinates. As a closed curve we use a rectangle which lies in the field. We designate the average of **A**$_z$ for the first side of the rectangle by **A**$_{z0}$. Then this average on side

3 has the value $\mathbf{A}_{z0} + \Delta y \, \partial \mathbf{A}_z/\partial y$, if Δy and Δz are small enough. We find $\mathbf{A}_{y0}$ and $\mathbf{A}_{y0} + \Delta z \, \partial \mathbf{A}_y/\partial z$ for the average of the tangential components on sides 2 and 4. The integral over the whole curve in the direction corresponding to a rotation from the y- to the z-axis is thus,

$$\int \mathbf{A}_s \, ds = + \mathbf{A}_{y0}\Delta y + \left(\mathbf{A}_{z0} + \frac{\partial \mathbf{A}_z}{\partial y} \Delta y \right)\Delta z$$

$$- \left(\mathbf{A}_{y0} + \frac{\partial \mathbf{A}_y}{\partial z} \Delta z \right)\Delta y - \mathbf{A}_{z0}\Delta z.$$

Dividing by $\Delta z \, \Delta y$ and proceeding to the limit, we obtain

$$\text{curl}_x \mathbf{A} = \frac{\partial \mathbf{A}_z}{\partial y} - \frac{\partial \mathbf{A}_y}{\partial z} \quad (3.16)$$

(According to our rule concerning signs, the positive x-axis is directed toward us in Fig. 26). By interchanging the subscripts we obtain

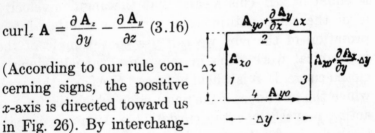

Fig. 26. Derivation of the formula for the curl

$$\text{curl}_y \mathbf{A} = \frac{\partial \mathbf{A}_x}{\partial z} - \frac{\partial \mathbf{A}_z}{\partial x}$$

$$\text{curl}_z \mathbf{A} = \frac{\partial \mathbf{A}_y}{\partial x} - \frac{\partial \mathbf{A}_x}{\partial y}.$$

$$(3.16a)$$

For the calculation of the curl in any other coordinate system, we must again select the curve according to the system. As an example, in cylindrical coordinates Fig. 27 shows that

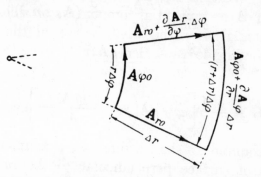

Fig. 27. Calculation of the curl in cylindrical coordinates

$$\int \mathbf{A}_s \, ds = \mathbf{A}_{r0}\Delta r + \left(\mathbf{A}_{\varphi 0} + \frac{\partial \mathbf{A}_\varphi}{\partial r}\,\Delta r\right)(r + \Delta r)\Delta\varphi$$

$$- \left(\mathbf{A}_{r0} + \frac{\partial \mathbf{A}_r}{\partial\varphi}\,\Delta\varphi\right)\Delta r - \mathbf{A}_{\varphi 0}r\Delta\varphi$$

and

$$\text{curl}_z\, \mathbf{A} = \frac{\partial \mathbf{A}_\varphi}{\partial r} + \frac{\mathbf{A}_\varphi}{r} - \frac{1}{r}\frac{\partial \mathbf{A}_r}{\partial\varphi}$$

$$= \frac{1}{r}\frac{\partial(r\mathbf{A}_\varphi)}{\partial r} - \frac{1}{r}\frac{\partial \mathbf{A}_r}{\partial\varphi}. \qquad (3.17)$$

The other components are

$$\text{curl}_\varphi\, \mathbf{A} = \frac{\partial \mathbf{A}_r}{\partial z} - \frac{\partial \mathbf{A}_z}{\partial r}$$

$$(3.17a)$$

$$\text{curl}_r\, \mathbf{A} = \frac{1}{r}\frac{\partial \mathbf{A}_z}{\partial\varphi} - \frac{\partial \mathbf{A}_\varphi}{\partial z}.$$

In spherical coordinates we have

$$\operatorname{curl}_\rho \mathbf{A} = \frac{1}{\rho \sin \vartheta} \left(\frac{\partial \mathbf{A}_\vartheta}{\partial \varphi} - \frac{\partial}{\partial \vartheta} (\mathbf{A}_\varphi \sin \vartheta) \right)$$

$$\operatorname{curl}_\varphi \mathbf{A} = \frac{1}{\rho} \frac{\partial \mathbf{A}_\rho}{\partial \vartheta} - \frac{1}{\rho} \frac{\partial (\rho \mathbf{A}_\vartheta)}{\partial \rho} \qquad (3.18)$$

$$\operatorname{curl}_\vartheta \mathbf{A} = \frac{1}{\rho} \left[\frac{\partial}{\partial \rho} (\rho \mathbf{A}_\varphi) - \frac{1}{\sin \vartheta} \frac{\partial \mathbf{A}_\rho}{\partial \varphi} \right].$$

As an example we shall deduce the ρ-component. The element of surface perpendicular to the radius ρ is bounded by two arcs of meridians with lengths $\rho \Delta \vartheta$ and two arcs of parallels with lengths $\rho \sin \vartheta \Delta \varphi$ and $\rho \sin (\vartheta + \Delta \vartheta) \Delta \varphi$ (Fig. 28). We have

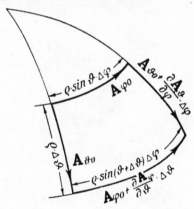

Fig. 28. Calculation of the curl in spherical coordinates

$$\int \mathbf{A}_s \, ds = -\left(\mathbf{A}_\varphi + \frac{\partial \mathbf{A}_\varphi}{\partial \vartheta} \Delta \vartheta \right) \rho \sin (\vartheta + \Delta \vartheta) \Delta \varphi$$

$$+ \left(\mathbf{A}_\vartheta + \frac{\partial \mathbf{A}_\vartheta}{\partial \varphi} \Delta \varphi \right) \rho \Delta \vartheta$$

$$+ \mathbf{A}_\varphi \rho \sin \vartheta \Delta \varphi - A_\vartheta \rho \Delta \vartheta.$$

Using the development $\sin(\vartheta + \Delta\vartheta) = \sin\vartheta + \Delta\vartheta\cos\vartheta$, dividing by the area $\rho^2 \sin\vartheta\Delta\vartheta\Delta\varphi$ and taking the limit for $\Delta\varphi\to 0$, $\Delta\vartheta\to 0$, we obtain the first of the formulae (3.18).

10. Divergence and curl of a gradient

Some combinations of our differential expressions are very important for physical applications. For example, we can investigate the special properties of the divergence and the curl of a vector field which is itself the gradient of a scalar or the curl of another vector.

Suppose we have $\mathbf{A} = \text{grad } \Phi$. Forming the divergence of this in rectangular coordinates, we obtain the following simple expression,

$$\text{div grad } \Phi = \frac{\partial}{\partial x}\left(\frac{\partial\Phi}{\partial x}\right) + \frac{\partial}{\partial y}\left(\frac{\partial\Phi}{\partial y}\right) + \frac{\partial}{\partial z}\left(\frac{\partial\Phi}{\partial z}\right)$$

$$= \frac{\partial^2\Phi}{\partial x^2} + \frac{\partial^2\Phi}{\partial y^2} + \frac{\partial^2\Phi}{\partial z^2}. \qquad (3.19)$$

This expression, which is named after Laplace, is most frequently encountered in the differential equations of physics. We designate it by $\Delta\Phi$ (or $\nabla^2\Phi$). Its representations in rectangular, cylindrical and spherical coordinates are

$$\Delta\Phi = \frac{\partial^2\Phi}{\partial x^2} + \frac{\partial^2\Phi}{\partial y^2} + \frac{\partial^2\Phi}{\partial z^2} \qquad (3.20)$$

$$\Delta\Phi = \frac{1}{r}\frac{\partial}{\partial r}\left(r\frac{\partial\Phi}{\partial r}\right) + \frac{1}{r^2}\frac{\partial^2\Phi}{\partial\varphi^2} + \frac{\partial^2\Phi}{\partial z^2} \qquad (3.21)$$

$$\Delta\Phi = \frac{1}{\rho^2}\frac{\partial}{\partial\rho}\left(\rho^2\frac{\partial\Phi}{\partial\rho}\right) + \frac{1}{\rho^2\sin\vartheta}\frac{\partial}{\partial\vartheta}\left(\frac{\partial\Phi}{\partial\vartheta}\sin\vartheta\right)$$

$$\text{(3.22)}$$

$$+ \frac{1}{\rho^2\sin^2\vartheta}\frac{\partial^2\Phi}{\partial\varphi^2}.$$

If we calculate the curl of grad Φ in rectangular coordinates we obtain

$$\text{curl}_x\,\text{grad}\,\Phi = \frac{\partial}{\partial y}\left(\frac{\partial\Phi}{\partial z}\right) - \frac{\partial}{\partial z}\left(\frac{\partial\Phi}{\partial y}\right)$$

$$= \frac{\partial^2\Phi}{\partial y\partial z} - \frac{\partial^2\Phi}{\partial z\partial y} = 0,$$

and the same is true for the other components. It is quite clear that this result is independent of the coordinate system and so we have, in general,

$$\text{curl grad}\,\Phi = 0. \qquad\text{(3.23)}$$

11. The divergence and the curl of a curl

If $\mathbf{B} = \text{curl}\,\mathbf{A}$ we see immediately that div $\mathbf{B} = 0$. For as we have seen earlier $\int \text{curl}\,\mathbf{A}\,df$ has the same value for two surfaces which are limited by the same curve (Fig. 29). These two surfaces enclose a region of space, and the vectors representing the curl on the surfaces are directed towards the interior for one surface and towards the

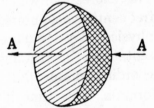

Fig. 29. Proof that curl $\mathbf{A} = 0$

exterior for the other. Since both integrals are equal, the outward flow is equal to the inward flow, and there is thus no source or sink so that the divergence is equal to zero. This can easily be verified by calculation in any coordinate system. The general formula is

$$\text{div curl } \mathbf{A} = 0. \tag{3.24}$$

We shall finally compute the curl of a curl in rectangular coordinates:

$$\text{curl}_x (\text{curl } \mathbf{A}) = \frac{\partial}{\partial y} (\text{curl}_z \mathbf{A}) - \frac{\partial}{\partial z} (\text{curl}_y \mathbf{A})$$

$$= \frac{\partial}{\partial y} \left(\frac{\partial \mathbf{A}_y}{\partial x} - \frac{\partial \mathbf{A}_x}{\partial y} \right) - \frac{\partial}{\partial z} \left(\frac{\partial \mathbf{A}_x}{\partial z} - \frac{\partial \mathbf{A}_z}{\partial x} \right)$$

$$= \frac{\partial}{\partial x} \left(\frac{\partial \mathbf{A}_y}{\partial y} + \frac{\partial \mathbf{A}_z}{\partial z} \right) - \frac{\partial^2 \mathbf{A}_x}{\partial y^2} - \frac{\partial^2 \mathbf{A}_x}{\partial z^2} .$$

By addition of

$$\frac{\partial^2 \mathbf{A}_x}{\partial x^2} - \frac{\partial^2 \mathbf{A}_x}{\partial x^2}$$

we obtain

$$\text{curl}_x (\text{curl } \mathbf{A}) = \frac{\partial}{\partial x} (\text{div } \mathbf{A}) - \Delta \mathbf{A}_x$$

or

$$\text{curl curl } \mathbf{A} = \text{grad div } \mathbf{A} - \Delta \mathbf{A}. \tag{3.25}$$

It is remarkable that the operator Δ appears in this formula. This time it operates on a vector, i.e., the single components of the vector.

We can also express the operators in (3.25) in any coordinate system. Then, however, we must remember that in this equation $\mathbf{A}$ stands for the Cartesian components A_r, A_ϑ, A_z. The computation is more complicated if we decompose $\mathbf{A}$ itself into the components corresponding to another system, for example, if we use A_r, A_φ, A_z in cylindrical coordinates.

12. Physical significance of the operator Δ

Since $\Delta\Phi$ is very important in the differential equations of physics we shall try to find a simple interpretation of this operator.

At a certain point 0 of the scalar field, Φ may have the value Φ_0. We construct a cube around 0, the sides of which are of length a. For the average value $\overline{\Phi}$ of Φ in this cube we have

$$\overline{\Phi}a^3 = \int\!\!\!\int\!\!\!\int_{-a/2}^{+a/2} \Phi \, dx \, dy \, dz.$$

The Taylor representation gives for any point x, y, z

$$\Phi = \Phi_0 + \left(\frac{\partial\Phi}{\partial x}\right)_0 x + \left(\frac{\partial\Phi}{\partial y}\right)_0 y + \left(\frac{\partial\Phi}{\partial z}\right)_0 z$$

$$+ \frac{1}{2}\left[\left(\frac{\partial^2\Phi}{\partial x^2}\right)_0 x^2 + \left(\frac{\partial^2\Phi}{\partial y^2}\right)_0 y^2 + \left(\frac{\partial^2\Phi}{\partial z^2}\right)_0 z^2\right]$$

$$+ \left(\frac{\partial^2\Phi}{\partial x\partial y}\right)_0 xy + \left(\frac{\partial^2\Phi}{\partial y\partial z}\right)_0 yz + \left(\frac{\partial^2\Phi}{\partial z\partial x}\right)_0 zx + \cdots.$$

If we integrate from $-a/2$ to $a/2$, the odd functions cancel out while from the other terms we obtain

$$\int\!\!\!\int\!\!\!\int_{-a/2}^{+a/2} x^2 \, dx \, dy \, dz = \frac{a^5}{12}, \text{ etc.}$$

We have finally

$$\overline{\Phi}a^3 = \Phi_0 a^3 + \frac{a^5}{24}\left(\frac{\partial^2\Phi}{\partial x^2} + \frac{\partial^2\Phi}{\partial y^2} + \frac{\partial^2\Phi}{\partial z^2}\right)_0$$

or

$$\overline{\Phi} - \Phi_0 = \frac{a^2}{24}\,\Delta_0\Phi.$$

The quantity ΔΦ therefore is a measure of the difference between the value of the scalar Φ at a point (0) and the average value of Φ in an infinitesimal neighbourhood of this point.

CHAPTER IV

THE SIMPLEST PARTIAL DIFFERENTIAL EQUATIONS OF PHYSICS

1. The potential equation

In many important cases, the difference between the local value of a function and the average in the neighbourhood is essential for describing the space-time development of the field. Thus the operator Δ appears very frequently in differential equations.

a. There exist fields such that the value of Φ at any point is equal to the average value for the neighbourhood. Then we have the Laplace equation

$$\Delta \Phi = 0. \tag{4.1}$$

An illustration is given by the gravitational field in a region free of mass. The force **K** which acts on a particle of unit mass in such a field is a function of the position of the particle only. In general, (positive or negative) work must be done to move the particle in the field. If the path along which the particle is moved is closed, however, the total work done is equal to zero. According to III 8, this can be expressed by

$$\text{curl } \mathbf{K} = 0. \tag{4.2}$$

This system of three equations (one for each component) can be reduced to one equation if we use (3.23). According to (3.23) equation (4.2) is satisfied by $\mathbf{K} =$ grad Φ. Now the gravitational field has the further property that its sources appear only where there is mass. Thus in empty space there are no sources in the gravitational field and we have

$$\text{div } \mathbf{K} = \text{div grad } \Phi = \Delta\Phi = 0. \qquad (4.3)$$

We shall show later that this equation is identical with Newton's law of gravitation (VII, 1).

We shall find fields of the same kind in electrostatics, in magnetostatics, and in fluid dynamics. Wherever there is a vector field the curl of which is equal to zero, we can reduce the number of unknowns from three to one by representing the field as the gradient of a scalar. Φ is called the "potential" of the vector field. The difference of potential between two points 0 and 1 is equal to

$$\Phi_1 - \Phi_0 = \int_0^1 \mathbf{K}_s \, ds$$

where the path of integration is any arbitrary curve joining the points 0 and 1. If $\mathbf{K}$ is a force, the integral represents the work to be done along the path, and in this case Φ is called the "potential energy" (of a unit mass in the case of the force of gravity).

b. There exist physical conditions such that the value of a scalar at a point differs from the average value in the neighbourhood. We then have the Poisson equation

$$\Delta\Phi = P, \qquad (4.4)$$

where P is a given function of the space. When the force is due to gravity, the density of mass ρ is proportional to the magnitude of the divergence of the force $\mathbf{K}$. Then we have,

$$\Delta\Phi = K\rho. \qquad (4.5)$$

(K = gravitational constant). The density of charge plays the same role in electrostatics, while there is no corresponding phenomenon in magnetostatics.

2. The equation of heat conduction

c. There are several physical processes in which the value of Φ at any point may be different from its average value in the neighbourhood at some time, but not for all values of time. In these cases this difference causes a tendency towards equalization with time. The smaller the local value than the average, the greater is its rate of increase with time. This is expressed mathematically by (k is factor of proportionality):

$$\Delta\Phi = k\frac{\partial\Phi}{\partial t}. \qquad (4.6)$$

The conduction of heat is the classical example of such a tendency towards equalization. Equation (4.6) is thus usually called the equation of heat conduction. In this particular example Φ is the temperature T. The heat flow $\mathbf{q} = -\lambda\,\mathrm{grad}\,T$ (see 3.3) causes an amount of heat $dV\,\mathrm{div}\,\mathbf{q}$ to leave any volume element dV in unit time, and consequently the temperature decreases at the rate $dV\,c\rho(\partial T/\partial t)$, where c is the specific heat and ρ is the density of the material. It follows then that

$$\mathrm{div}\,\mathbf{q} = -\lambda\Delta T = -c\rho\frac{\partial T}{\partial t}$$

or

$$\Delta T = \frac{c\rho}{\lambda}\frac{\partial T}{\partial t}. \qquad (4.7)$$

$\lambda/c\rho$ is called "heat conductivity".

The laws of diffusion are expressed by the same differential equation. In this case Φ is the density of the diffusing material. This density changes at a rate proportional to the difference between its local value and the average value. The speed of diffusion is also proportional to the rate of change of density, as in the case of heat flow.

From the physical standpoint, friction in liquids and gases also is a similar phenomenon. This analogy is important in the kinetic theory of gases and supplies a relation between the constants of heat conduction and friction of the materials in question. These latter problems are rather difficult from the mathematical point of view, however, since these phenomena of friction cannot be described by a scalar or a vector, but require the concept of a tensor. Thus we cannot consider this problem here.

3. Wave equation

d. Finally, the deviation of a local value from the average in the neighbourhood can also have the same effect as a displacement from the position of equilibrium in the phenomena of oscillation (II 12). A force can appear which tends to give the variable the average value and so to restore the system to the equilibrium position. Thus we obtain a motion for which the dependence on time is expressed by a quantity analogous to the acceleration, namely the second derivative. This equation must be of the form

$$\Delta\Phi = \frac{1}{c^2}\frac{\partial^2\Phi}{\partial t^2}. \tag{4.8}$$

Here $1/c^2$ is written as a square since it is a positive factor. The value of Φ is "accelerated" and hence increases at those places where it is smaller than the average. The essential properties of this differential equation can be found by comparing it with mechanical oscillations (II 12). As a result of the acceleration, $\partial\Phi/\partial t$ is not equal to zero in the equilibrium position as it is in (4.6). The system "moves" through the position of equilibrium and the same process begins anew. The variable Φ oscillates about its value in the equilibrium position. (4.8) is the general wave equation. The constant c is the speed of propagation, as we shall see in (V 5).

4. Differential equations of perfect fluids

The hydrodynamical field can be described by the hydrostatic pressure p (which is a scalar) and the velocity $\mathbf{v}$ (vector). We shall express both quantities as functions of position and time and not as functions of a fixed particle in the fluid. At a certain position in space there are different particles at different times, thus p and $\mathbf{v}$ are functions of the time and the coordinates of a point which does not move with the fluid. We have one scalar and one vector differential equation according to the number of unknowns. The first equation expresses the theorem of the conservation of mass. The mass contained in a volume element is equal to $\rho\, dV$, where ρ is the density. The mass which leaves the element in unit time is dV div $(\rho\mathbf{v})$. This decreases the mass contained in the element which results in a decrease of the density of the remaining fluid in the volume element. In terms of the derivative of the density, the decrease of mass in dV in unit time is equal to $-dV\ \partial\rho/\partial t$. Hence the equation of continuity of fluid dynamics has the form

$$\frac{\partial\rho}{\partial t} + \text{div } (\rho\mathbf{v}) = 0. \tag{4.9}$$

If the fluid is incompressible ($\rho = $ const), it has the simpler form

$$\text{div } \mathbf{v} = 0. \tag{4.9a}$$

The vector equation of hydrodynamics contains the fundamental Newtonian law (2.3) for a single volume element dV. The mass is $\rho\ dV$. Now in the Newton equation the acceleration is the derivative of the velocity of a definite particle and *not* the derivative of the velocity at a fixed point. This change of velocity is composed of two parts; first there is the change in velocity at the position of the particle, and second the change in velocity due to the change in position of the particle. The first change is expressed by the partial derivative $\partial\mathbf{v}/\partial t$, while the second is equal to

$$\frac{\partial\mathbf{v}}{\partial x}\frac{dx}{dt} + \frac{\partial\mathbf{v}}{\partial y}\frac{dy}{dt} + \frac{\partial\mathbf{v}}{\partial z}\frac{dz}{dt}. \tag{4.10}$$

In this equation, $dx/dt,\ \cdots$ denote the derivatives of the position of the particle with respect to the time. That means that they are identical with the components of the velocity $\mathbf{v}$ at the point. If we denote these components by u, v, w, the three components of the expression (4.10) are

$$u \frac{\partial u}{\partial x} + v \frac{\partial u}{\partial y} + w \frac{\partial u}{\partial z} \,,$$

$$u \frac{\partial v}{\partial x} + v \frac{\partial v}{\partial y} + w \frac{\partial v}{\partial z} \,, \qquad (4.10a)$$

$$u \frac{\partial w}{\partial x} + v \frac{\partial w}{\partial y} + w \frac{\partial w}{\partial z} \,.$$

As an abbreviation we shall write the vector symbol $(\mathbf{v}\ \mathrm{grad})\ \mathbf{v}$ for the three expressions (4.10a). The force acting on the volume element dV consists of a volume force (for example the weight) $\mathbf{K}\ dV$ and the resultant of the pressure forces on the surface of the element, which is equal to $-dV\ \mathrm{grad}\ p$. We can derive this result by considering the element $dx\ dy\ dz$ in Fig. 30. The

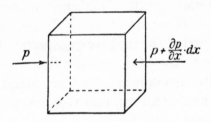

Fig. 30. Hydrostatic pressure

pressure is normal to the surface, so that the force $p\ dy\ dz$ acts in the direction of the positive x-axis and the force $-[p + (\partial p/\partial x)\ dx]\ dy\ dz$ in the negative direction. The resultant component in the x-direction is $-(\partial p/\partial x)\ dy\ dz$.

Thus we obtain the vector equation of fluid dynamics (Euler's equation):

$$\rho \left\{ \frac{\partial \mathbf{v}}{\partial t} + (\mathbf{v}\ \mathrm{grad})\mathbf{v} \right\} = \mathbf{K} - \mathrm{grad}\ p. \qquad (4.11)$$

If the fluid is incompressible (e.g., water), ρ is a constant, while if the fluid is compressible ρ is a given function of p for adiabatic processes, for instance. In the following we shall consider only the case $\rho = \mathrm{const.}$

5. Vortices

Wherever possible we must reduce these four differential equations with four unknowns to one equation containing one unknown only for mathematical treatment. First we shall eliminate the pressure from (4.11) by calculating the curl of the right hand term (curl grad $p = 0$ according to (3.23)). If the volume force $\mathbf{K}$ is derived from a potential Ω (see IV 1), it too drops out and we have

$$\frac{\partial}{\partial t}(\mathrm{curl}\ \mathbf{v}) + \mathrm{curl}\ \{(\mathbf{v}\ \mathrm{grad})\mathbf{v}\} = 0. \qquad (4.12)$$

We shall write this equation in Cartesian coordinates. The following calculations, however, are only made for the z-component. This equals

$$\frac{\partial}{\partial t}\left(\frac{\partial u}{\partial y} - \frac{\partial v}{\partial x} \right) + \frac{\partial}{\partial y}\left\{ u\frac{\partial u}{\partial x} + v\frac{\partial u}{\partial y} + w\frac{\partial u}{\partial z} \right\}$$

$$- \frac{\partial}{\partial x}\left\{ u\frac{\partial v}{\partial x} + v\frac{\partial v}{\partial y} + w\frac{\partial v}{\partial z} \right\} = 0$$

or

$$\frac{\partial}{\partial t}\left(\frac{\partial u}{\partial y} - \frac{\partial v}{\partial x} \right) + \frac{\partial u}{\partial y}\frac{\partial u}{\partial x} + \frac{\partial v}{\partial y}\frac{\partial u}{\partial y} + \frac{\partial w}{\partial y}\frac{\partial u}{\partial z} +$$

$$+ u \frac{\partial^2 u}{\partial x \partial y} + v \frac{\partial^2 u}{\partial y^2} + w \frac{\partial^2 u}{\partial y \partial z}$$

$$- \frac{\partial u}{\partial x} \frac{\partial v}{\partial x} - \frac{\partial v}{\partial x} \frac{\partial v}{\partial y} - \frac{\partial w}{\partial x} \frac{\partial v}{\partial z}$$

$$- u \frac{\partial^2 v}{\partial x^2} - v \frac{\partial^2 v}{\partial x \partial y} - w \frac{\partial^2 v}{\partial x \partial z} = 0$$

or, in a clearer form,

$$\left(\frac{\partial}{\partial t} + u \frac{\partial}{\partial x} + v \frac{\partial}{\partial y} + w \frac{\partial}{\partial z} \right) \left(\frac{\partial u}{\partial y} - \frac{\partial v}{\partial x} \right)$$

$$+ \left(\frac{\partial u}{\partial y} - \frac{\partial v}{\partial x} \right) \left(\frac{\partial u}{\partial x} + \frac{\partial v}{\partial y} \right) + \frac{\partial w}{\partial y} \frac{\partial u}{\partial z} - \frac{\partial w}{\partial x} \frac{\partial v}{\partial z} = 0.$$

By use of

$$\operatorname{div} \mathbf{v} = \frac{\partial u}{\partial x} + \frac{\partial v}{\partial y} + \frac{\partial w}{\partial z} = 0, \qquad (4.9a)$$

and addition of

$$+ \frac{\partial w}{\partial y} \frac{\partial w}{\partial x} - \frac{\partial w}{\partial y} \frac{\partial w}{\partial x} + \left(\frac{\partial u}{\partial y} - \frac{\partial v}{\partial x} \right) \frac{\partial w}{\partial z} - \left(\frac{\partial u}{\partial y} - \frac{\partial v}{\partial x} \right) \frac{\partial w}{\partial z},$$

we finally obtain the simpler form

$$\left(\frac{\partial}{\partial t} + u \frac{\partial}{\partial x} + v \frac{\partial}{\partial y} + w \frac{\partial}{\partial z} \right) \left(\frac{\partial u}{\partial y} - \frac{\partial v}{\partial x} \right)$$

$$- \left(\frac{\partial u}{\partial y} - \frac{\partial v}{\partial x} \right) \frac{\partial w}{\partial z} - \left(\frac{\partial v}{\partial z} - \frac{\partial w}{\partial y} \right) \frac{\partial w}{\partial x}$$

$$- \left(\frac{\partial w}{\partial x} - \frac{\partial u}{\partial z} \right) \frac{\partial w}{\partial y} = 0. \qquad (4.13)$$

This is an equation for the three components of the curl. In addition we have two other equations. Now, the first term in (4.13) is equal to the derivative with respect to time of the curl at a fixed particle (according to page 70) and (4.13) expresses the fact that this derivative is equal to zero if the curl itself is equal to zero. The physical significance of the curl is the "vortex" (see III 8). Thus we see that a particle of the fluid which is not rotating at a certain instant will never rotate. This is true as long as our assumptions of perfect fluid and conservative volume forces hold. If a fluid particle moves in a curved path it does not necessarily mean that the particle itself rotates. If, as shown in Fig. 31, we produce

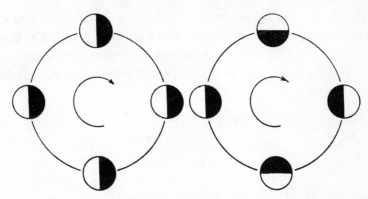

Fig. 31a. Circular motion without rotation (Ferris wheel)

Fig. 31b. Circular motion with rotation (moon circling the earth)

a vortex at the origin, the other particles which were not rotating before and which are moved only by the pressure, will remain without vorticity. They move as shown in Fig. 31a, not as in Fig. 31b.

6. Potential flow

While it is quite possible to treat vortex flows from (4.13), we shall only consider here flows without vorticity, since these represent a very clear example of the application of differential equations. If curl $\mathbf{v} = 0$ everywhere at a certain instant, the same will be true for any time. It follows then from (3.23) (and in analogy to (4.3)), that $\mathbf{v}$ is the gradient of a scalar Φ which is called the "velocity potential"

$$\mathbf{v} = \operatorname{grad} \Phi. \tag{4.14}$$

From the equation of continuity (4.9a) it follows that

$$\operatorname{div} \operatorname{grad} \Phi = \Delta\Phi = 0. \tag{4.15}$$

Furthermore we have the following boundary conditions: a. at a rigid wall, the fluid cannot penetrate into the wall and thus there is no velocity component normal to the wall; b. the pressure is constant at a free surface.

By a simple calculation we obtain

$$u \frac{\partial u}{\partial x} + v \frac{\partial u}{\partial y} + w \frac{\partial u}{\partial z} = \frac{\partial \Phi}{\partial x} \frac{\partial}{\partial x} \left(\frac{\partial \Phi}{\partial x} \right)$$

$$+ \frac{\partial \Phi}{\partial y} \frac{\partial}{\partial x} \left(\frac{\partial \Phi}{\partial y} \right) + \frac{\partial \Phi}{\partial z} \frac{\partial}{\partial x} \left(\frac{\partial \Phi}{\partial z} \right)$$

$$= \frac{1}{2} \frac{\partial}{\partial x} \left\{ \left(\frac{\partial \Phi}{\partial x} \right)^2 + \left(\frac{\partial \Phi}{\partial y} \right)^2 + \left(\frac{\partial \Phi}{\partial z} \right)^2 \right\} \tag{4.15a}$$

or $(\mathbf{v}\operatorname{grad})\,\mathbf{v} = \frac{1}{2}\operatorname{grad} v^2$. If we replace $\mathbf{v}$ by $\operatorname{grad} \Phi$ in (4.11) and use (4.15a) we obtain

$$\rho \left[\operatorname{grad} \frac{\partial \Phi}{\partial t} + \frac{1}{2} \operatorname{grad} \left\{ \left(\frac{\partial \Phi}{\partial x} \right)^2 + \left(\frac{\partial \Phi}{\partial y} \right)^2 + \left(\frac{\partial \Phi}{\partial z} \right)^2 \right\} \right]$$

$$= - \operatorname{grad} \Omega - \operatorname{grad} p.$$

We integrate this once, obtaining

$$\rho\left[\frac{\partial\Phi}{\partial t} + \frac{1}{2}\left\{\left(\frac{\partial\Phi}{\partial x}\right)^2 + \left(\frac{\partial\Phi}{\partial y}\right)^2 + \left(\frac{\partial\Phi}{\partial z}\right)^2\right\}\right]$$

$$+ \Omega + p = \text{const.}$$

(4.16)

Hence we find p if we know Φ and if the constant is determinable from the given values of Φ and p at some point.

Flows without vorticity (potential flows) are only a special simplified case of real flows. However, a great number of practical problems can be solved by a potential flow approximation. Airfoil theory and related questions in the theory of airplanes, propellers, and turbines as well as surface waves and fluid jets are treated in just this way.

7. Differential equations of electrodynamics

The electromagnetic field in empty space is described by the two vectors of the electric and magnetic field (**E** and **H**). The differential equations of this field can be derived according to Maxwell from two empirical facts. The first is Faraday's law of induction: the rate of change $\partial\mathbf{H}/\partial t$ of the magnetic field is associated with an electric field **E** such that

$$\frac{1}{c}\frac{\partial\mathbf{H}}{\partial t} = -\text{ curl } \mathbf{E}.$$

(4.17)

The constant c is a factor of proportionality and has the dimension of a velocity, if **E** and **H** are defined by means of the forces in the electrostatic and magnetostatic field. This factor, which we shall again meet in (4.18), is just equal to the velocity of light. This fact was one of the first which led to the electromagnetic theory of light.

The second empirical fact which was generalized into a fundamental law by Maxwell concerns the generation of a magnetic field by an electric current. The connection between both is an example of the concept of the curl. Originally the differential equation is

$$\frac{1}{c} \mathbf{J} = \operatorname{curl} \mathbf{H}$$

where c is the same quantity as in (4.17) if the density $\mathbf{J}$ of current is also defined in the electrostatic system. Maxwell, with reasoning based on certain properties of alternating currents and with the intention of finding an analogy between light and electromagnetic fields, completed this equation by introducing the concept of a "displacement current" $\partial \mathbf{E}/\partial t$. This current should be capable of generating a magnetic field in the same way as an ordinary current $\mathbf{J}$ and analogous to $\partial \mathbf{H}/\partial t$ in (4.17).

The differential equation now becomes

$$\frac{1}{c}\left(\frac{\partial \mathbf{E}}{\partial t} + \mathbf{J}\right) = \operatorname{curl} \mathbf{H}. \qquad (4.18)$$

According to the electronic theory, one can write the current density $\mathbf{J}$ as the product of the density of charge ρ by the velocity $\mathbf{v}$ of the charge.

From (4.17) and (3.24) we obtain

$$\frac{\partial}{\partial t} (\operatorname{div} \mathbf{H}) = 0$$

which means that div $\mathbf{H}$ is independent of the time. According to our experience no magnetic sources (charges) exist, thus we have

$$\text{div } \mathbf{H} = 0. \tag{4.19}$$

If we take the divergence of both sides of (4.18) we obtain the "continuity equation"

$$\frac{\partial}{\partial t} (\text{div } \mathbf{E}) + \text{div } \mathbf{J} = 0. \tag{4.20}$$

The density of charge ρ is defined by the following equation,

$$\text{div } \mathbf{E} = \rho. \tag{4.21}$$

With $\mathbf{J} = \rho\mathbf{v}$, (4.21) takes the form (4.9) of the continuity equation of hydrodynamics. This analogy is already expressed in the word "current".

8. The field equation in material bodies

Hitherto we have only talked about the field in empty space under the influence of electric currents and charges. From the standpoint of the electronic theory, this case covers all possibilities, for this theory only considers currents and charges and explains the influence which these bodies have upon the field by assuming distributions of charges and currents in the material bodies. The exact manner in which these currents and charges are distributed in the bodies is the object of special theories which lack of space does not allow us to consider here.

The older Maxwell theory avoids these difficulties by

assigning a generalized form to the fundamental equation whereby they contain certain constants of the material. These general equations containing the permeability μ, the dielectric constant ϵ and the conductivity σ, are

$$\frac{\mu}{c}\frac{\partial \mathbf{H}}{\partial t} = - \operatorname{curl} \mathbf{E}, \qquad \operatorname{div}(\mu \mathbf{H}) = 0$$

$$\tag{4.22}$$

$$\frac{1}{c}\left[\epsilon\frac{\partial \mathbf{E}}{\partial t} + \sigma \mathbf{E}\right] = \operatorname{curl} \mathbf{H}, \qquad \operatorname{div}(\epsilon \mathbf{E}) = 0.$$

We shall now try to simplify the system of the Maxwell equations by the elimination of variables. For this purpose, however, we shall again consider the electromagnetic field in empty space.

9. Energy theorem

We can obtain a simple relation if we form the scalar product of (4.18) with $\mathbf{E}$ and of (4.17) with $\mathbf{H}$ and use the relation

$$\mathbf{E}\cdot \operatorname{curl} \mathbf{H} - \mathbf{H}\cdot \operatorname{curl} \mathbf{E} = - \operatorname{div}(\mathbf{E} \times \mathbf{H})$$

(This relation can be easily verified by using rectangular coordinates). We then obtain the following equation

$$\frac{1}{2c}\frac{\partial}{\partial t}(\mathbf{H}^2 + \mathbf{E}^2) + \frac{1}{c}\mathbf{E}\cdot \mathbf{J} + \operatorname{div}(\mathbf{E} \times \mathbf{H}) = 0. \tag{4.23}$$

This equation is an energy theorem: $\frac{1}{2}\mathbf{E}^2$ is the electric energy, $\frac{1}{2}\mathbf{H}^2$ the magnetic energy per unit volume, $\mathbf{E}\cdot \mathbf{J}$ is the Joule heat which is produced in a unit volume in unit time, $c\operatorname{div}(\mathbf{E} \times \mathbf{H})$ is the energy leaving the volume in unit time and thus it follows that $c\mathbf{E} \times \mathbf{H}$ is the flow of energy through the surface in unit time. This vector is called the "Poynting vector".

10. Electromagnetic waves

Whenever we have $\rho = 0$ and $\mathbf{J} = 0$ the Maxwell equations can be reduced to a single equation containing only one unknown. If in

$$\frac{1}{c} \frac{\partial \mathbf{H}}{\partial t} = - \operatorname{curl} \mathbf{E}$$

$$\frac{1}{c} \frac{\partial \mathbf{E}}{\partial t} = \operatorname{curl} \mathbf{H}$$

we take the curl of the first equation and the derivative with respect to time of the second and then multiply the latter with $1/c$ and add, we obtain

$$\frac{1}{c^2} \frac{\partial^2 \mathbf{E}}{\partial t^2} = - \operatorname{curl} \operatorname{curl} \mathbf{E}.$$

Using (3.25) and div $\mathbf{E} = 0$, we obtain the wave equation

$$\frac{1}{c^2} \frac{\partial^2 \mathbf{E}}{\partial t^2} = \Delta \mathbf{E}. \tag{4.24}$$

Each component of $\mathbf{E}$ satisfies this equation. The same equation is valid for $\mathbf{H}$. This result is of great theoretical significance, since it proves the existence of electromagnetic waves and shows that their velocity of propagation is equal to the velocity of light. The propagation of light can therefore be treated by the Maxwell theory.

If we eliminate **H** from (4.22) in the same way we obtain

$$\frac{\epsilon\mu}{c^2}\frac{\partial^2 \mathbf{E}}{\partial t^2} + \frac{\sigma\mu}{c}\frac{\partial \mathbf{E}}{\partial t} = \Delta\mathbf{E}. \tag{4.25}$$

In this differential equation there is a term which corresponds to a wave having a velocity $c/(\epsilon\mu)^{\frac{1}{2}}$ and another term which corresponds to a damping of the oscillations. If we compare this term with (4.7) we see that the damping is greater the smaller the conductivity of the material.

11. Electromagnetic potentials

We can obtain another simplification of the Maxwell equations by introducing the concept of potentials. In this respect the static cases present nothing new, since if curl **E** = 0 or curl **H** = 0 the situation is similar to that previously considered for the gravitational field or for the (potential) flow of a fluid. Let us introduce a potential Φ such that $\mathbf{E} = -\text{grad }\Phi$. We then obtain from div **E** = 0

$$\Delta\Phi = 0. \tag{4.26}$$

In the general case we can introduce a so called "vector potential" by

$$\mathbf{H} = \text{curl }\mathbf{A} \tag{4.27}$$

This is possible since div **H** = 0 (see (3.24)). The introduction of **A** does not have an immediate advantage, since **A** is again a vector. Instead of the three original unknowns we have three others. However, if we introduce this expression of **H** in (4.17) we obtain

$$\operatorname{curl}\left(\frac{1}{c}\frac{\partial \mathbf{A}}{\partial t}\right) = -\operatorname{curl} \mathbf{E}.$$

From this we can not conclude that $\mathbf{E} = -\partial \mathbf{A}/c\ \partial t$. Since the curl of a gradient is always equal to zero [(3.23)], two quantities with equal curls may differ by the gradient of a scalar. Thus we have

$$\mathbf{E} = -\frac{1}{c}\frac{\partial \mathbf{A}}{\partial t} - \operatorname{grad} \Phi. \qquad (4.28)$$

If we introduce these relations into the two other Maxwell equations (4.18) and (4.21), we obtain

$$-\frac{1}{c}\frac{\partial}{\partial t}(\operatorname{div} \mathbf{A}) - \Delta\Phi = \rho,$$

$$-\frac{1}{c^2}\frac{\partial^2 \mathbf{A}}{\partial t^2} - \frac{1}{c}\frac{\partial}{\partial t}\operatorname{grad}\Phi + \frac{1}{c}\mathbf{J} \qquad (4.29)$$

$$= \operatorname{grad}\operatorname{div}\mathbf{A} - \Delta\mathbf{A}.$$

Since the potentials have only to be chosen such that (4.27) and (4.28) are satisfied, we are free to prescribe another relation between the two potentials. We chose a relation that simplifies (4.29) essentially, namely

$$\frac{1}{c}\frac{\partial\Phi}{\partial t} + \operatorname{div}\mathbf{A} = 0. \qquad (4.30)$$

In this case we obtain a couple of equations from (4.29) which again are very similar to the wave equation

$$\frac{1}{c^2}\frac{\partial^2 \mathbf{A}}{\partial t^2} - \Delta\mathbf{A} = \frac{1}{c}\mathbf{J},$$

$$\frac{1}{c^2}\frac{\partial^2\Phi}{\partial t^2} - \Delta\Phi = \rho. \qquad (4.31)$$

These four differential equations contain only four unknowns, while the original ones contained six. The importance of the symbol Δ should be noted, and also the importance of differential equations of the type we found in IV 1 to 3.

12. Boundary conditions

Let us consider a surface element f which contains a part of the boundary between two materials (Fig. 32) whose extension perpendicular to the boundary is infinitely small in comparison to its extension parallel to the boundary. If the difference of the components parallel to the boundary ($\mathbf{E}_{p_1}$ and $\mathbf{E}_{p_2}$ in Fig. 32) were finite, the curl would be infinite. For the line integral $\int \mathbf{E}_s \, ds$ would be finite while the area f is infinitesimal. Since $\partial(\mu H)/\partial t$ cannot be infinite in (4.22), we have

Fig. 32. The electric force at the boundary of two materials

$$\mathbf{E}_{p_1} = \mathbf{E}_{p_2} . \tag{4.32}$$

The same holds true for the magnetic components which are parallel to the boundary because the left hand term of the other equations (4.22) also cannot be infinite.

If we apply the two divergence equations to a prismatic region of base f (Fig. 32) and height h (normal to plane of Fig. 32), we obtain two boundary conditions for the normal components of $\mathbf{E}$ and $\mathbf{H}$. Since div $\mathbf{H} = 0$, the two normal components cannot be different from each other, and thus we have

$$\mu_1 \mathbf{H}_{n1} = \mu_2 \mathbf{H}_{n2} . \qquad (4.33)$$

On the other hand we have

$$\text{div } (\epsilon \mathbf{E}) fh = (\epsilon_2 \mathbf{E}_{n2} - \epsilon_1 \mathbf{E}_{n1}) lh,$$

and therefore

$$\epsilon_2 \mathbf{E}_{n2} - \epsilon_1 \mathbf{E}_{n1} = \lim_{f \to 0} \rho \, \frac{f}{l} = \omega. \qquad (4.34)$$

ω can be different from zero, since at the boundary of the two materials there exist densities of charge so large that in the limit they may approach f/l. Charges of this kind (finite charge in an infinitesimal volume) are called "surface charges".

CHAPTER V

SOLUTIONS BY EIGENFUNCTIONS

1. The product method

There may exist solutions of a partial differential equation which are the product of several functions, each of which depends only on one variable. This idea often allows us to reduce the solution of a partial differential equation to the solution of several ordinary ones. A solution of this kind is not general, of course, and the method can only be used if the boundary conditions satisfy certain conditions of symmetry and homogeneity. In many practical cases, however, the method is sufficiently general.

We demonstrate the method with the potential equation

$$\frac{\partial^2 u}{\partial x^2} + \frac{\partial^2 u}{\partial y^2} + \frac{\partial^2 u}{\partial z^2} = 0 \qquad (5.1)$$

We try $u = XYZ$, where X is a function of x alone, Y of y alone and Z of z alone. If we denote differentiation by primes, we obtain from (5.1)

$$X''YZ + Y''XZ + Z''XY = 0 \qquad (5.2)$$

After division by XYZ we obtain

$$\frac{X''}{X} + \frac{Y''}{Y} + \frac{Z''}{Z} = 0.$$

Now X''/X is a function of x alone etc. These three functions of different variables can have the sum zero only if they are constants. Thus we have

$$\frac{X''}{X} = -\alpha, \qquad \frac{Y''}{Y} = -\beta, \qquad \frac{Z''}{Z} = -\gamma, \quad (5.3)$$

where the constants α, β, γ satisfy the condition

$$\alpha + \beta + \gamma = 0. \tag{5.4}$$

The negative signs in (5.3) were chosen for practical reasons.

Now the three ordinary differential equations (5.3) are to be solved; their solutions involve six constants of integration. The nature of the boundary conditions determines whether or not the constants can be determined and if they are sufficient to satisfy the boundary conditions. This also decides whether or not the method can be used at all. We shall now specialize our problem physically and formulate several boundary conditions.

2. Example: steady flow of heat

The equation $\Delta u = 0$ gives the temperature u in a body in which there is a steady distribution of heat, i.e. throughout which the temperature depends only on the position but not on time. We assume that the body is rectangular and that its edges have the lengths a, b, c. We chose a rectangular coordinate system which has its axes parallel to the edges of the body. Four sides of the body may be completely insulated so that there is no heat flowing through them. One side ($x = a$) may be subjected to a constant temperature (zero). On the remaining side ($x = 0$) the temperature may be given by a function $u = f(y, z)$. What is the temperature in the interior of the body? We have the six boundary conditions

$$u = f(y, z) \text{ for } x = 0, u = 0 \text{ or } X = 0 \text{ for } x = a.$$

Furthermore, since the flow of heat is proportional to grad u (according to (3.5)) we have

$$\frac{\partial u}{\partial y} = 0, \text{ or } Y' = 0 \text{ for } y = 0 \text{ and for } y = b$$

$$\tag{5.5}$$

$$\frac{\partial u}{\partial z} = 0, \text{ or } Z' = 0 \text{ for } y = 0 \text{ and for } z = c.$$

These boundary conditions are homogeneous and linear except for the first. This means that they contain the first power of the unknown in each term.

We shall first make use of the second equation (5.3): $Y'' + \beta Y = 0$ with the boundary conditions $Y' = 0$ for $y = 0$ and $y = b$. The most general solution is

$$Y = A \sin (\beta^{\frac{1}{2}} y) + B \cos (\beta^{\frac{1}{2}} y).$$

In order to satisfy $Y' = 0$ for $y = 0$, we must have $A = 0$, and since

$$B\beta^{\frac{1}{2}} \sin (\beta^{\frac{1}{2}} b) = 0$$

(from the second condition), we have either $B = 0$ or $\sin (\beta^{\frac{1}{2}} b) = 0$. In the first case ($B = 0$) we have $Y = 0$ which is of no use. In the second case we have

$$\beta^{\frac{1}{2}} = n\pi/b \quad (n = \text{arbitrary integer}). \tag{5.6}$$

At the beginning of our computation we introduced β as an arbitrary constant. It has been determined to a certain extent by the calculation. (5.6) gives an infinity of possible values for β. They are called the "eigenvalues". To each eigenvalue corresponds an eigenfunction $\cos(n\pi y/b)$, which satisfies the second equation in (5.3) and its boundary conditions. Moreover, each one of the infinitely many eigenfunctions multiplied by an arbitrary constant (B_n), is a solution. We now have the problem of deciding which of the eigenfunctions we can use in our case and how to determine the constants B_n.

First, however, we note that in a similar way we find that the eigenvalues

$$\gamma^{\frac{1}{2}} = m\pi/c \quad (m = \text{arbitrary integer}) \qquad (5.7)$$

and the eigenfunctions $\cos(m\pi z/c)$ correspond to the equation

$$Z'' + \gamma Z = 0 \text{ with } Z' = 0 \text{ for } z = 0 \text{ and } z = c.$$

From (5.6), (5.7) and (5.4) it follows that

$$\alpha = -\left(\frac{n\pi}{b}\right)^2 - \left(\frac{m\pi}{c}\right)^2 \qquad (5.8)$$

If we introduce the above into $X'' + \alpha X = 0$, we obtain

$$X'' - \left[\left(\frac{n\pi}{b}\right)^2 + \left(\frac{m\pi}{c}\right)^2\right]X = 0$$

with the boundary condition $X = 0$ for $x = a$. With the abbreviation

$$\left(\left(\frac{n\pi}{b}\right)^2 + \left(\frac{m\pi}{c}\right)^2\right)^{\frac{1}{2}} = \nu_{mn}$$

the solution is

$$X = A_{mn}[\cosh(\nu_{mn}x) - \coth(\nu_{mn}a) \sinh(\nu_{mn}x)]. \quad (5.9)$$

In this way we have found a double infinitude of solutions $u = XYZ$ of the differential equation with the homogeneous boundary conditions. Since the differential equation is linear the sum of several solutions is again a solution and now we must find a linear combination of solutions which also satisfies the inhomogeneous boundary condition for $x = 0$.

If $f(y, z)$ is of the form

$$f(y, z) = A_{mn} \cos \frac{n\pi}{b} y \cos \frac{m\pi}{c} z$$

the problem is, however, already solved by one of the particular solutions of the homogeneous problem.

3. Fourier series

Since the particular solutions of the differential equation can be additively combined to yield the general solution, we have the following result: if the function $f(y, z)$ can be represented in the form

$$f(y, z) = \sum_{m=0}^{\infty} \sum_{n=0}^{\infty} A_{mn} \cos \frac{n\pi y}{b} \cos \frac{m\pi z}{c}, \quad (5.10)$$

then the temperature field is

$$u = \sum_{m=0}^{\infty} \sum_{n=0}^{\infty} A_{mn}[\cosh \nu_{mn}x$$

$$- \coth \nu_{mn}a \sinh \nu_{mn}x] \cos \frac{n\pi y}{b} \cos \frac{m\pi z}{c} \quad (5.11)$$

where

$$\nu_{mn} = \left(\left(\frac{n\pi}{b}\right)^2 + \left(\frac{m\pi}{c}\right)^2\right)^{\frac{1}{2}}.$$

Thus our method is sufficient for all functions which can be expanded into a trigonometric series of the form (5.10).

For the sake of simplicity we now assume that in (5.10) all coefficients A_{mn} are equal to zero, when m is different from one. This means that $f(y, z)$ has the form $F(y) \cos (\pi z/c)$ and the problem is reduced to the expansion of $F(y)$ into a series

$$F(y) = \sum_{n=0}^{\infty} A_n \cos \frac{n\pi y}{b}. \tag{5.12}$$

Series of the type (5.12) are called Fourier series, after the mathematician who first used them and established their general properties.

The functions on the right-hand side of (5.12) are periodic. The greatest period is (if we omit $n = 0$) the one that corresponds to $n = 1$. Its magnitude is $2b$. The other periods are equal to $2b$ divided by some integer. The function on the right hand side of (5.12) is thus periodic with period $2b$. The function $F(y)$ is given for one half of the period only, namely between $y = 0$ and $y = b$. For our purposes it is sufficient if the series in (5.12) represents $F(y)$ in this interval. The values outside of this interval do not concern us. To extend $F(y)$ from the interval $(0, b)$ to an interval which is the whole period, i.e. $(-b, b)$, we may define $F(-y) = F(y)$ for any y in $(0, b)$. Indeed, any function represented by (5.12) is an even function, since only terms containing cosines appear in the series. The function can be defined over the whole y-axis in a unique way, since it must be periodic.

First we obtain a simple representation for the A_n: multiplying equation (5.12) by $\cos (l\pi y/b)$ ($l =$ integer) and integrating from $y = 0$ to $y = 2b$, we obtain

$$\int_0^{2b} F(y) \cos \frac{l\pi y}{b} \, dy$$

$$= \sum_{n=0}^{\infty} A_n \int_0^{2b} \cos \frac{n\pi y}{b} \cos \frac{l\pi y}{b} \, dy. \qquad (5.13)$$

Now we have

$$\int_0^{2b} \cos \frac{n\pi y}{b} \cos \frac{l\pi y}{b} \, dy$$

$$= \frac{1}{2} \int_0^{2b} \left[\cos (n + l) \frac{\pi y}{b} + \cos (n - l) \frac{\pi y}{b} \right] dy \quad (5.14)$$

and all these integrals are equal to zero except in the case $n = l$. In this case the integral in (5.14) reduces to

$$\int_0^{2b} dy = 2b.$$

This operation makes all terms in (5.13), for which $n \neq l$ equal to zero, and the remaining term is $A_l b$.

This enables A_n to be calculated in a simple way:

$$A_n = \frac{1}{b} \int_0^{2b} F(y) \cos \frac{n\pi y}{b} \, dy. \qquad (5.15)$$

EXAMPLE 91

Let us introduce $\eta = \pi y/b$ as a new variable, whose period is equal to 2π instead of $2b$. We then obtain the nicer mathematical form

$$A_n = \frac{1}{\pi} \int_0^{2\pi} F(\eta) \cos (n\eta) \, d\eta. \qquad (5.16)$$

The case $n = 1$ is a special one. If in (5.12) we take the average value of all terms on the right side, we obtain zero as the result, since each cosine term is equally often positive as negative. For $n = 0$, $\cos 0 = 1$ and thus we have

$$A_0 = \frac{1}{2b} \int_0^{2b} F(y) \, dy = \frac{1}{2\pi} \int_0^{2\pi} F(\eta) \, d\eta. \quad (5.17)$$

We thus have a method of calculation for the coefficients A_n. No restrictions on $F(y)$ were necessary if only the integrals in (5.15) and (5.17) have a meaning, i.e., $F(y)$ must be integrable. However continuity and differenciability at every point are not necessary.

We must omit here the proof of the statement that the series with the calculated coefficients has $F(y)$ as limit. This method for the calculation of the coefficients is valid in much more general cases than our example, as we shall show later.

4. Example

We shall now carry through the computations for a specific example. The temperature may be a linearly dependent function of y for $x = 0$. Then we have $F(y) = C(b - y)$. This function and its continuation as an even periodic function is represented in Fig. 33.

According to this representation we have $F(y) = C(y - b)$ in $(b, 2b)$. From (5.17) follows that

$$A_0 = \frac{C}{2b} \left[\int_0^b (b - y)\, dy + \int_b^{2b} (y - b)\, dy \right] = C\,\frac{b}{2}.$$

From (5.15)

$$A_n = \frac{C}{b} \left[\int_0^b (b - y) \cos \frac{n\pi y}{b}\, dy \right.$$

$$+ \left. \int_b^{2b} (y - b) \cos \frac{n\pi y}{b}\, dy \right]$$

$$= 2\,\frac{Cb}{n^2 \pi^2} (1 - \cos n\pi)$$

or

$$A_n = 4\,\frac{Cb}{n^2 \pi^2} \qquad \text{for odd } n,$$

$$A_n = 0 \qquad \text{for even } n.$$

Thus we have the Fourier series

$$F(y) = 4\,\frac{Cb}{\pi^2} \left[\frac{\pi^2}{8} + \frac{1}{1^2} \cos \frac{\pi y}{b} + \frac{1}{3^2} \cos \frac{3\pi y}{b} \right.$$

(5.18)

$$\left. + \frac{1}{5^2} \cos \frac{5\pi y}{b} \cdots \right]$$

and the solution of our problem is

$$u = \frac{4Cb}{\pi^2} \cos \frac{\pi z}{c} \left[\frac{\pi^2}{8} \left(\cosh \frac{\pi x}{c} - \coth \frac{\pi a}{c} \sinh \frac{\pi x}{c} \right) \right.$$

$$+ \frac{1}{1^2} \left\{ \cosh \pi \left(\frac{1}{b^2} + \frac{1}{c^2} \right)^{\frac{1}{2}} x - \coth \pi \left(\frac{1}{b^2} + \frac{1}{c^2} \right)^{\frac{1}{2}} a \right.$$

$$\left. \sinh \pi \left(\frac{1}{b^2} + \frac{1}{c^2} \right)^{\frac{1}{2}} x \right\} \cos \frac{\pi y}{b}$$

$$+ \frac{1}{3^2} \left\{ \cosh \pi \left(\frac{9}{b^2} + \frac{1}{c^2} \right)^{\frac{1}{2}} x - \coth \pi \left(\frac{9}{b^2} + \frac{1}{c^2} \right)^{\frac{1}{2}} a \right.$$

$$\left. \left. \sinh \pi \left(\frac{9}{b^2} + \frac{1}{c^2} \right)^{\frac{1}{2}} x \right\} \cos \frac{3\pi y}{b} + \cdots \right] \quad (5.19)$$

This gives us the temperature at any point x, y, z in the body. Fig. 33 shows how rapidly the series converges.

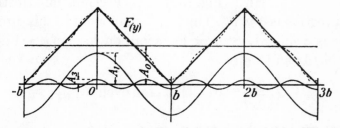

Fig. 33. Decomposition of a function $F(y)$ into a Fourier series
—— Sum of the first three terms of the Fourier expansion

5. Oscillations of a string

The mathematical method of Fourier series becomes very clear in the theory of acoustic oscillations. The decomposition of a sound into fundamental and harmonic tones is an idea familiar to the reader. The importance of trigonometric functions in the calculation we just completed suggests taking an example from the theory of oscillations in which we have already encountered these functions (II 12). The equation (4.8) is valid for all instruments which generate tones. According to the particular case under consideration, this equation may be derived from the theory of elastic materials (strings, diaphragms) or the theory of compressible fluids (for pipes).

We shall consider the simple example of a string which is fixed at the points $x = 0$ and $x = l$ and is under the tension S (the force per unit cross section). We seek u, the perpendicular displacement from the equilibrium position as a function of the position x and the time t. The differential equation can be deduced by examining one element with mass $\rho \, dx$ (ρ = mass of per unit length) (Fig. 34). Its acceleration in the u-direction is $\partial^2 u / \partial t^2$. The force component in this direction is $S \sin \varphi_1 - S \sin \varphi_0$. For small angles, $\sin \varphi \sim \tan \varphi = \partial u / \partial x$ and we have

$$S \left\{ \left(\frac{\partial u}{\partial x} \right)_1 - \left(\frac{\partial u}{\partial x} \right)_0 \right\} = S \frac{\partial}{\partial x} \left(\frac{\partial u}{\partial x} \right) dx.$$

From Newton's law it follows that

$$\rho \frac{\partial^2 u}{\partial t^2} = S \frac{\partial^2 u}{\partial x^2}. \tag{5.20}$$

If we put $S/\rho = c_2$ we obtain the simplest form of (4.8):

$$\frac{\partial^2 u}{\partial t^2} = c^2 \frac{\partial^2 u}{\partial x^2}. \tag{5.21}$$

If we put $u = X(x)T(t)$ here, we obtain the equations

$$\frac{X''}{X} = -\alpha \qquad \text{and} \qquad \frac{T''}{T} = -\alpha c^2, \qquad (5.22)$$

where α is an undetermined constant and the negative sign was chosen in order to simplify the equations. To the first equation (5.22) there correspond the boundary conditions

$$u = 0 \qquad \text{for } x = 0 \text{ and } x = l.$$

From $X = A \sin (\alpha^{\frac{1}{2}}x) + B \cos (\alpha^{\frac{1}{2}}x)$ we again obtain either the trivial solution $X = 0$ unless the number α equals one of the eigenvalues $n^2\pi^2/l^2$ (n = integer). The eigenfunctions are $\sin (n\pi x/l)$, where $n\pi/l$ is the space frequency of the oscillations. The wave length is $2l/n$, which is equal to twice the length of the string or an integral part of it (Fig. 35). This is the well known representation of fundamental and harmonic

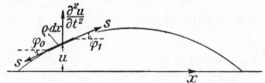

Fig. 34. Oscillating string

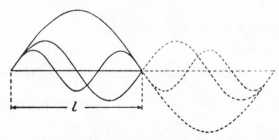

Fig. 35. Fundamental and harmonic oscillations

oscillations. The time frequencies follow immediately from the second equation (5.22), the solutions of which are

$$T = A_n \cos \frac{n\pi ct}{l} + B_n \sin \frac{n\pi ct}{l}.$$

The frequencies are equal to $n\pi c/l$, and the period of oscillation is $2l/nc$. The velocity of propagation is generally equal to wave length/time of oscillation, which is equal to c (see IV 3).

We obtain the constants A_n and B_n here from the values corresponding to $t = 0$. The position u of the string and the speed $\partial u/\partial t$ must be given as functions of x at the beginning of the oscillation. In the case of plugging the initial position is given, in the case of striking the initial velocity. The precise manner of excitation differs widely for the various string instruments; it determines the constants A_n and B_n and hence the intensity of the harmonics and the quality of the sound.

If the initial conditions are $u = f(x)$ and $\partial u/\partial x = 0$, all B_n are equal to 0 and $f(x)$ must have the form of a sum

$$\sum_{n=1}^{\infty} A_n \sin \frac{n\pi x}{l}.$$

If the initial conditions are $u = 0$ and $\partial u/\partial x = g(x)$, the A_n are equal to zero and

$$g(x) = \sum_{n=1}^{\infty} B_n \frac{nc}{l} \sin \frac{n\pi x}{l}.$$

The coefficients of a sine series can be calculated in the same way as in the case of a cosine series. If the initial position and the initial velocity are both different from zero, the best thing to do is to represent the solution as a sum of two functions for one of which the initial velocity is zero and for the other of which the initial position is equal to zero. There are instruments which are able to decompose an oscillation into "partial oscillations" as they occur in the Fourier series. These are mostly based on the phenomenon of resonance. This is the principle of the ear. Other natural means are dispersion where the partial oscillations have different speeds, and finally damping where the harmonic oscillations are annihilated faster than the fundamental oscillation. We shall later consider an example of this latter phenomenon.

6. Generalization

We shall now show the extent of our method. Our previous considerations seem to have been dependent on the use of trigonometric functions which seem to satisfy the relation

$$\int_0^{2\pi} \cos n\eta \, \cos l\eta \, d\eta = 0 \qquad \text{for } l \neq n,$$

by mere chance, thus resulting in a great simplification. It can easily be seen that the method is not restricted to pure cosine series, but that it can be extended to pure sine or even mixed series with the aid of

$$\int_0^{2\pi} \sin n\eta \, \sin l\eta \, d\eta = 0 \qquad \text{for } l \neq n$$

and

$$\int_0^{2\pi} \cos n\eta \sin l\eta \, d\eta = 0 \qquad \text{for all } l \text{ and } n.$$

Also the simplification from (5.10) to (5.12) was made only for convenience. In the general case we could determine the coefficients A_{mn} in the same way, since

$$\int_0^{2\pi} \int_0^{2\pi} \cos n\eta \, \cos m\zeta \, \cos l\eta \, \cos k\zeta \, d\eta \, d\zeta = 0,$$

unless $n = l$ and $m = k$.

This double integral is equal to π^2 if $n = l$ and $m = k$ and therefore we have in (5.10)

$$A_{mn} = \frac{1}{bc} \int_0^{2b} \int_0^{2c} f(y,z) \cos \frac{n\pi y}{b} \cos \frac{m\pi z}{c} \, dy \, dz. \quad (5.23)$$

In order to see the general content of these relations, we must ask how we happened to use the functions $\cos(n\pi y/b) \cos(m\pi z/c)$. We obtained them as eigenfunctions of a differential equation which was of the form

$$\Delta u = 0 \qquad \text{or} \qquad \Delta u = \frac{1}{c^2} \frac{\partial^2 u}{\partial t^2}$$

with certain boundary conditions. These homogeneous linear differential equations from IV 1-3 (the method naturally does not work in the case of equation (4.5)) can always be transformed into the form

$$\Delta v = \lambda v, \qquad (5.24)$$

by representing the unknown function as a product.

Here v depends on one, two, or three variables; Δv has one of the forms given in III 10 and the region under consideration is a curve, a surface, or a volume according to the number of variables. The constant λ corresponds to the constants α, β, γ in our examples and has different values which can be used for solutions. They are again called eigenvalues. We shall choose the function v such that it will satisfy homogeneous linear boundary conditions only. The most general condition of this kind is

$$hv + k\,\frac{\partial v}{\partial n} = 0. \qquad (5.25)$$

Here n is the normal to the boundary of the region. In the example of the temperature field, the expression YZ in (5.2) corresponds to the present v. According to (5.2) and (5.3) we have the equation

$$\Delta v = Y''Z + Z''Y = -\frac{X''}{X}\,YZ = \alpha v.$$

The region of the function v is the y, z-plane between the limits 0 and b and 0 and c respectively. The boundary conditions are linear and homogeneous: $\partial u/\partial n = 0$.

However the functions Y and Z themselves satisfy the conditions (5.24) and (5.25), since we have

$$\Delta Y = Y'' = -\left(\frac{X''}{X} + \frac{Z''}{Z}\right)Y = (\alpha + \gamma)Y.$$

This time the region is a line, namely the y-axis between 0 and b, and the boundary conditions are $Y' = 0$ corresponding to (5.25) with $h = 0$. In the example of the oscillating string X satisfies all conditions for v, since we have

$$\Delta X = X'' = -\alpha X;$$

The region is the segment from $x = 0$ to $x = l$ and the boundary conditions are $X = 0$, corresponding to $k = 0$ in (5.25).

7. Green's theorem and orthogonality

There exist certain theorems concerning functions of the type v which satisfy (5.24) and (5.25). We shall find them with the aid of Green's theorem which follows from the theorem of Gauss (3.12). In (3.12) we write

$$\mathbf{A} = \Phi \operatorname{grad} \Psi - \Psi \operatorname{grad} \Phi, \qquad (5.26)$$

instead of $\mathbf{A}$, where Φ and Ψ are scalars. Since, for example, we have

$$\operatorname{div}\{\Phi \operatorname{grad} \Psi\}$$

$$= \frac{\partial}{\partial x}\left(\Phi \frac{\partial \Psi}{\partial x}\right) + \frac{\partial}{\partial y}\left(\Phi \frac{\partial \Psi}{\partial y}\right) + \frac{\partial}{\partial z}\left(\Phi \frac{\partial \Psi}{\partial z}\right)$$

$$= \Phi \Delta \Psi + \frac{\partial \Phi}{\partial x}\frac{\partial \Psi}{\partial x} + \frac{\partial \Phi}{\partial y}\frac{\partial \Psi}{\partial y} + \frac{\partial \Phi}{\partial z}\frac{\partial \Psi}{\partial z},$$

in rectangular coordinates, then

$$\operatorname{div} \cdot \mathbf{A} = \Phi \Delta \Psi - \Psi \Delta \Phi.$$

Furthermore

$$\mathbf{A}_n = \Phi \frac{\partial \Psi}{\partial n} - \Psi \frac{\partial \Phi}{\partial n}.$$

We thus obtain Green's theorem

$$\int (\Phi\Delta\Psi - \Psi\Delta\Phi)\, dV = \int \left(\Phi\,\frac{\partial\Psi}{\partial n} - \Psi\,\frac{\partial\Phi}{\partial n}\right) df. \quad (5.27)$$

Here V is any region (one, two, or three-dimensional) and f is the boundary of the region.

We shall now apply (5.27) for two eigenfunctions v_l and v_m which satisfy (5.24) and (5.25). According to (5.24) we introduce in

$$\int (v_l\Delta v_m - v_m\Delta v_l)\, dV = \int \left(v_l\,\frac{\partial v_m}{\partial n} - v_m\,\frac{\partial v_l}{\partial n}\right) df \quad (5.28)$$

the expressions

$$\Delta v_l = \lambda_l v_l \qquad \text{and} \qquad \Delta v_m = \lambda_m v_m$$

and notice that according to (5.25) the integrand on the right hand side is equal to zero. Thus we have

$$(\lambda_l - \lambda_m)\int v_l v_m\, dV = 0. \quad (5.29)$$

If now λ_l and λ_m are two different eigenvalues, we have

$$\int v_l v_m\, dV = 0, \quad (5.30)$$

and this is a generalization of a formula which we have already met and which enabled us to calculate the Fourier coefficients in a simple way. The property of the eigenfunctions which is expressed in (5.30) is called "orthogonality". If $m = l$, (5.30) is not true, of course, since $\int v_m^2\, dV$ is positive.

8. Particular solutions in rectangular Cartesian coordinates

By the use of rectangular coordinates the solutions of the equations for X, Y, Z in our examples were expressed by trigonometric functions, and the same is true for T in the oscillation problem. Exponential functions appear in the solution of the equation for the conduction of heat. For if we write $u = vT(t)$ in the equation

$$\Delta u = \frac{c\rho}{\lambda} \frac{\partial u}{\partial t},$$

we obtain

$$\frac{T'}{T} = \text{const} = -\alpha,$$

the solution of which is given by

$$T = e^{-\alpha t}. \tag{5.31}$$

9. Particular solutions in cylindrical coordinates

If the problem has cylindrical symmetry, we shall express Δv in cylindrical coordinates according to (3.21). Equation (5.24) then takes the following form

$$\frac{1}{r} \frac{\partial}{\partial r}\left(r \frac{\partial v}{\partial r}\right) + \frac{1}{r^2} \frac{\partial^2 v}{\partial \varphi^2} + \frac{\partial^2 v}{\partial z^2} = \lambda v. \tag{5.32}$$

If we put $v = R(r)\Phi(\varphi)Z(z)$ in (5.32) and divide by $R\Phi Z$, we obtain

$$\frac{1}{rR} \frac{d}{dr}\left(r \frac{dR}{dr}\right) + \frac{1}{r^2\Phi} \Phi'' + \frac{Z''}{Z} = \lambda. \tag{5.33}$$

Since Z''/Z and Φ''/Φ are independent of z and of φ respectively, the following relations follow from (5.33)

$$\frac{Z''}{Z} = -\alpha \quad \text{and} \quad \frac{\Phi''}{\Phi} = -\beta. \quad (5.34)$$

These relations are satisfied by trigonometric functions if α and β are positive, and by hyperbolic functions if they are negative. β can only be positive, however.

From (5.33) and (5.34) we obtain the equation

$$\frac{1}{r}\frac{d}{dr}\left(r\frac{dR}{dr}\right) - \left\{(\lambda + \alpha) + \frac{\beta}{r^2}\right\}R = 0$$

for R. If we put $-(\lambda + \alpha) = k^2$ and $\beta = p^2$ we have

$$\frac{d^2R}{dr^2} + \frac{1}{r}\frac{dR}{dr} + \left(k^2 - \frac{p^2}{r^2}\right)R = 0. \quad (5.35)$$

This can be simplified by introducing the variable $kr = \rho$. Thus,

$$\frac{d^2R}{d\rho^2} + \frac{1}{\rho}\frac{dR}{d\rho} + \left(1 - \frac{p^2}{\rho^2}\right)R = 0. \quad (5.36)$$

This is Bessel's differential equation. Its solutions are called Bessel functions. If one wants to use these functions for calculations, one must use tables as for the trigonometric functions. p is called the order of the Bessel function. Since (5.36) is of order two, there must exist two independent Bessel functions of order p. If p is rational these two functions are called "of orders $+p$ and $-p$" and are denoted by $J_p(\rho)$ and $J_{-p}(\rho)$. For integer p's the tables usually contain a Bessel function $J_p(\rho)$ and a "Neumann function" $K_p(\rho)$ which is sometimes denoted by $N_p(\rho)$ or $Y_p(\rho)$.

There will be a short discussion in a later section on the most important methods in the theory of these functions (V 11 and 12).

The special case $\lambda + \alpha = 0$ can occur if, for example, we have the equation $\Delta v = 0$ and v is independent of z. The equation then has the form

$$\frac{d^2R}{dr^2} + \frac{1}{r}\frac{dR}{dr} - \frac{p^2}{r^2}R = 0 \qquad (5.37)$$

and the two particular solutions are $R = r^p$ and $R = r^{-p}$.

10. Particular solutions in spherical coordinates

If the problem has spherical symmetry, we use equation (3.22):

$$\frac{1}{\rho^2}\frac{\partial}{\partial\rho}\left(\rho^2\frac{\partial v}{\partial\rho}\right) + \frac{1}{\rho^2\sin\vartheta}\frac{\partial}{\partial\vartheta}\left(\sin\vartheta\frac{\partial v}{\partial\vartheta}\right)$$
$$+ \frac{1}{\rho^2\sin^2\vartheta}\frac{\partial^2 v}{\partial\varphi^2} = \lambda v. \qquad (5.38)$$

We put $v = R(r)\,\Theta(\vartheta)\,\Phi(\varphi)$ and divide by $R\Theta\Phi$. Thus,

$$\frac{1}{\rho^2 R}\frac{d}{d\rho}(\rho^2 R') + \frac{1}{\rho^2\,\Theta\sin\vartheta}\frac{d}{d\vartheta}(\Theta'\sin\vartheta)$$
$$+ \frac{1}{\rho^2\,\Phi\sin^2\vartheta}\Phi'' = \lambda. \qquad (5.39)$$

We now obtain that Φ''/Φ is independent of φ and consequently is a constant $(= -\alpha)$. The left-hand side of (5.39) is thus the sum of a function of ρ and a function of ϑ,

$$\left[\frac{1}{R}\frac{d}{d\rho}(\rho^2 R') - \lambda\rho^2\right]$$

$$+ \left[\frac{1}{\Theta \sin\vartheta}\frac{d}{d\vartheta}(\Theta' \sin\vartheta) - \frac{\alpha}{\sin^2\vartheta}\right] = 0. \tag{5.40}$$

Since, however, the sum is equal to zero, each term must be zero. The general theory of these problems is difficult and we shall consider only special cases.

First we shall simplify the equation

$$\frac{1}{R}\frac{d}{d\rho}(\rho^2 R') - \lambda\rho^2 = \text{const.} = \beta \tag{5.41}$$

by taking the special case $\lambda = 0$ which corresponds to the differential equation $\Delta v = 0$. It is easy to see that

$$\frac{d}{d\rho}(\rho^2 R) = \rho\frac{d^2}{d\rho^2}(\rho R).$$

The differential equation

$$\rho\frac{d^2}{d\rho^2}(\rho R) = \beta R \tag{5.42}$$

can be solved by setting $R = \rho^\nu$. We then obtain

$$\nu(\nu + 1) = \beta. \tag{5.43}$$

If we now write $\beta = m(m + 1)$, we have

$$\nu = m \qquad \text{or} \qquad \nu = -m - 1. \tag{5.44}$$

The other limiting case $\beta = 0$ corresponds to oscillation and heat problems which are independent of ϑ and φ. The equation is

$$\frac{d^2}{d\rho^2}(\rho R) = \rho R \lambda; \qquad (5.45)$$

The solutions are $\rho R = \sin(\lambda^{\frac{1}{2}}\rho)$ and $\cos(\lambda^{\frac{1}{2}}\rho)$ or

$$R = \frac{\sin(\lambda^{\frac{1}{2}}\rho)}{\rho} \quad \text{and} \quad \frac{\cos(\lambda^{\frac{1}{2}}\rho)}{\rho} \qquad (5.46)$$

The second equation following from (5.40) is

$$\frac{1}{\sin\vartheta}\frac{d}{d\vartheta}(\Theta'\sin\vartheta) + \left(\gamma - \frac{\alpha}{\sin^2\vartheta}\right)\Theta = 0. \quad (5.47)$$

Here we shall only consider the case $\alpha = 0$, that is, the case of independence of the "longitude".

In order to find the usual form we put $\gamma = m(m + 1)$. This is somewhat arbitrary as long as we do not know anything about γ and m. However, if $\lambda = 0$ and $\alpha = 0$ for the problem under consideration, m has the same significance as in (5.44), since in this case we have $\gamma = \beta$. We obtain

$$\frac{1}{\sin\vartheta}\frac{d}{d\vartheta}\left(\frac{d\Theta}{d\vartheta}\sin\vartheta\right) + m(m + 1)\Theta = 0 \quad (5.48)$$

or with $x = \cos\vartheta$

$$\frac{d}{dx}\left[(1 - x^2)\frac{d\Theta}{dx}\right] + m(m + 1)\Theta = 0. \quad (5.49)$$

The solutions of this differential equation are called spherical functions and are denoted by $P_m(x)$ and $Q_m(x)$, where m is the order of the function. Since $\cos\vartheta$ varies between -1 and $+1$ and is an even function, it suffices to know the spherical functions in the interval $0 \leq x \leq 1$ or $0 \leq \vartheta \leq \pi/2$. There also exist tables for these functions.

The solutions of (5.47) with arbitrary α can be expressed by spherical functions. They are called associated Legendre functions. Again lack of space does not allow us to consider this case here.

11. Solution of ordinary differential equations by expansion in series

We have twice encountered differential equations whose solutions are not elementary and known from previous courses. We found it necessary to use tables for practical calculations. We shall now use these functions as an example in order to demonstrate the procedure for finding the properties of functions which satisfy a given differential equation.

We assume that the solution of the differential equation (5.36)

$$\frac{d^2R}{d\rho^2} + \frac{1}{\rho}\frac{dR}{d\rho} + \left(1 - \frac{p^2}{\rho^2}\right)R = 0 \qquad (5.50)$$

can be expanded in a power series about the point $\rho = 0$. The coefficients of this series are unknown and will be determined by introducing the series into the equation. Assume that the series is of the form

$$R = \rho^\nu + a_1\rho^{\nu+1} + a_2\rho^{\nu+2} + \cdots$$
$$+ a_n\rho^{\nu+n} + \cdots . \qquad (5.51)$$

The coefficients $a_1, \cdots$ and the first exponent ν are unknown. From the series we find

$$\frac{dR}{d\rho} = \nu\rho^{\nu-1} + a_1(\nu + 1)\rho^\nu + \cdots + a_n(\nu + n)\rho^{\nu+n-}$$

$$a_{n+1}(\nu + n + 1)\rho^{\nu+n} + \cdots$$

$$\frac{d^2R}{d\rho^2} = \nu(\nu - 1)\rho^{\nu-2} + a_1(\nu + 1)\nu\rho^{\nu-1} + \cdots$$

$$a_{n+1}(\nu + n + 1)(\nu + n)\rho^{\nu+n-1}$$

$$a_{n+2}(\nu + n + 2)(\nu + n + 1)\rho^{\nu+n} + \cdots$$

By introducing these expressions in (5.50) and grouping the terms of equal powers of ρ we obtain

$$\rho^{\nu-2}[\nu(\nu - 1) + \nu - p^2]$$

$$+ \rho^{\nu-1}[a_1(\nu + 1)\nu + a_1(\nu + 1) - a_1 p^2]$$

$$+ \rho^\nu[a_2(\nu + 2)(\nu + 1)$$

$$+ a_2(\nu + 2) - a_2 p^2 + 1] + \cdots \tag{5.52}$$

$$+ \rho^{\nu+n}[a_{n+2}(\nu + n + 2)(\nu + n + 1)$$

$$+ a_{n+2}(\nu + n + 2) - a_{n+2}p^2 + a_n] + \cdots = 0.$$

If this equation is to be satisfied for all values of ρ in a certain neighbourhood of $\rho = 0$, then the coefficient of each power of ρ must be equal to zero. The first coefficient contains only the first exponent ν as an unknown. Thus we find

$$\nu = \pm p. \tag{5.53}$$

We now have two solutions in the form of a series, as was to be expected. One begins with ρ^ν and the other with $\rho^{-\nu}$. One is equal to zero for $\rho = 0$, the other has an infinite value for $\rho = 0$. From the second coefficient it follows that $a_1 = 0$. If in the third we put $\nu = \pm p$, we obtain

$$a_2\{(\pm p + 2)(\pm p + 2) - p^2\} + 1 = 0$$

or

$$a_2 = -\frac{1}{2(\pm 2p + 2)}.$$

Similarly we obtain the general recurrence formula

$$a_{n+2} = -\frac{a_n}{(n + 2)(\pm 2p + n + 2)}. \tag{5.54}$$

Thus the two series representing the solutions of our differential equation are

$$R_1 = \rho^p \left\{ 1 - \frac{\rho^2}{2(2p + 2)} + \frac{\rho^4}{2 \cdot 4(2p + 2)(2p + 4)} \right.$$

$$\left. - \frac{\rho^6}{2 \cdot 4 \cdot 6 \cdot (2p + 2)(2p + 4)(2p + 6)} + \cdots \right.$$

$$\tag{5.55}$$

$$R_2 = \rho^{-p} \left\{ 1 - \frac{\rho^2}{2(2 - 2p)} + \frac{\rho^4}{2 \cdot 4(2 - 2p)(2 - 4p)} \right.$$

$$\left. + \frac{\rho^6}{2 \cdot 4 \cdot 6 \cdot (2 - 2p)(4 - 2p)(6 - 2p)} + \cdots \right.$$

In the tables of Bessel functions these functions are multiplied by a conventionally selected constant. The series are convergent for each value of ρ. If ρ is large, however, they converge very slowly.

The series R_2 has no meaning if p is a positive integer, nor has R_1 if p is a negative integer. In these cases we can only use one series as a solution. Also for $p = 0$ we have only one solution. Here we can find the second solution in the following way; p shall not be equal to zero initially, but merely small. R_1 and R_2 do not differ much from each other. The difference is of the same order of magnitude as p. If, therefore, we take the limit as $p \to 0$

$$\lim_{p \to 0} \frac{R_1 - R_2}{2p},$$

we obtain a new solution of the equation which is identical to the one we previously called the Neumann function $K_0(\rho)$. The limit of the first term of the series is

$$\lim_{p \to 0} \frac{\rho^p - \rho^{-p}}{2p} = \lim_{p \to 0} \frac{e^{p \, \log \, \rho} - e^{-p \, \log \, \rho}}{2p}$$

$$= \lim_{p \to 0} \frac{(1 + p \log \rho + \cdots) - (1 - p \log \rho + \cdots)}{2p}$$

$$= \log \rho,$$

and the second term is

$$\lim_{p \to 0} \frac{1}{2p} \left[\frac{\rho^{p+2}}{2(2 + 2p)} - \frac{\rho^{-p+2}}{2(2 - 2p)} \right]$$

$$= \lim_{p \to 0} \frac{\rho^2}{8p} \left[\frac{1 + p \log \rho + \cdots}{1 + p} \right.$$

$$\left. - \frac{1 - p \log \rho + \cdots}{1 - p} \right] \tag{5.56}$$

$$= \lim_{p \to 0} \frac{\rho^2}{8p} \Big[(1 + p \log \rho + \cdots)(1 - p + \cdots)$$

$$- (1 - p \log \rho + \cdots)(1 + p + \cdots) \Big]$$

$$= \frac{\rho^2}{4} (\log \rho - 1)$$

etc. We do not require the complete series, since we can already see the most important property. The series begins with the term $\log \rho$ and therefore for $\rho = 0$ becomes infinite as the logarithm and not like any power ρ^ν. This is the reason why we did not find this solution amongst the power series.

We shall now use this method of expansion into a series to determine the spherical functions which are defined by

$$\frac{d}{dx} \Big[(1 - x^2) \frac{d\Theta}{dx} \Big] + m(m + 1)\Theta = 0. \quad (5.57)$$

The series

$$\Theta = x^\nu + a_1 x^{\nu+1} + \cdots + a_n x^{\nu+n} + \cdots \quad (5.58)$$

gives us the relations

$$\nu(\nu - 1) = 0, \quad \text{i.e., } \nu_1 = 0 \quad \text{and} \quad \nu_2 = 1$$

$$a_1 = a_3 = \cdots = 0$$

$$a_2 = - \frac{m(m + 1) - \nu(\nu + 1)}{(\nu + 1)(\nu + 2)}$$

and

$$a_{n+2} = - \frac{m(m + 1) - (\nu + n)(\nu + n + 1)}{(\nu + n + 1)(\nu + n + 2)} a_n . \quad (5.59)$$

Thus we obtain the two solutions

$$\theta_1 = 1 - \frac{m(m + 1) - 0 \cdot 1}{1 \cdot 2} x^2$$

$$+ \frac{\{m(m + 1) - 0 \cdot 1\}\{m(m + 1) - 2 \cdot 3\}}{1 \cdot 2 \cdot 3 \cdot 4} x^4$$

$$- \cdots$$

$$(5.60)$$

$$\theta_2 = x - \frac{m(m + 1) - 1 \cdot 2}{2 \cdot 3} x^3$$

$$+ \frac{\{m(m + 1) - 1 \cdot 2\}\{m(m + 1) - 3 \cdot 4\}}{2 \cdot 3 \cdot 4 \cdot 5} x^5$$

$$- \cdots$$

A most important property of these functions is that one of the series has a finite number of terms whenever m is an integer. (This is always so in physical problems.) The coefficients of $x^{\nu + n + 2}$ and all the higher powers are equal to zero if $\nu + n = m$. This behaviour is visible in θ_1 for even m, and in θ_2 for odd m. We have, for example, for $m = 2$

$$\theta_1 = 1 - \frac{2 \cdot 3}{1 \cdot 2} x^2,$$

and for $m = 3$

$$\theta_2 = x - \frac{3 \cdot 4 - 1 \cdot 2}{2 \cdot 3} x^3.$$

These finite series (after multiplication by a normalization factor) are called spherical functions of the first kind and are denoted by $P_m(x)$. The infinite series are called spherical functions of the second kind and are denoted by $Q_m(x)$. They have infinite values for $x = 1$.

12. Asymptotic expansions

The expansion which we have found is sufficient for the determination of the properties of spherical functions, since these functions are defined in the interval $0 < x < 1$ only. However, in the case of Bessel functions, the argument can have greater values and in some cases it may not be possible to use the series. In such cases the differential equation can be integrated "asymptotically" for very great values of the variable. We shall demonstrate this method with the Bessel functions. In equation (5.50),

$$\frac{d^2 R}{d\rho^2} + \frac{1}{\rho} \frac{dR}{d\rho} + \left(1 - \frac{p^2}{\rho^2}\right)R = 0, \qquad (5.61)$$

we shall first neglect the terms containing the large values ρ and ρ^2 in the denominator. We then have the equation.

$$\frac{d^2 R}{d\rho^2} + R = 0,$$

a solution of which is $R = e^{\pm i\rho}$. Now we shall try to find a solution of (5.61) which can be represented as the product of this R by a series in decreasing powers of ρ

$$R = e^{i\rho}[\rho^{\nu} + a_1\rho^{\nu-1} + a_2\rho^{\nu-2} + \cdots]. \quad (5.62)$$

(We do not continue to write $\pm i$, since the two corresponding solutions will simply be conjugate.) We obtain

$$\frac{dR}{d\rho} = e^{i\rho}[\rho^{\nu}i + \rho^{\nu-1}(ia_1 + \nu)$$

$$+ \rho^{\nu-2}(ia_2 + (\nu - 1)a_1) + \cdots]$$

$$\frac{d^2R}{d\rho^2} = e^{i\rho}[\rho^{\nu}(-1) + \rho^{\nu-1}(-a_1 + 2i\nu)$$

$$+ \rho^{\nu-2}\{-a_2 + i(\nu - 1)a_1$$

$$+ (\nu - 1)(ia_1 + \nu)\} + \cdots]$$

If we introduce these expressions in (5.61), we obtain $e^{i\rho}$ multiplied by a descending power series. The coefficient of each power of ρ in this series must be equal to zero (as in V 11). The coefficient of ρ^{ν} is identically zero. The next term is equal to $-a_1 + 2i\nu + i + a_1$. Thus we obtain $\nu = -1/2$. The coefficient of $\rho^{\nu-2}$ is

$$-a_2 + (\nu - 1)(2ia_1 + \nu) + ia_1 + \nu + a_2 - p^2$$

and it follows that

$$a_1 = \frac{i(\nu^2 - p^2)}{2\nu - 1} = i\,\frac{4p^2 - 1}{8}$$

Thus we obtain the asymptotic series

$$R = \frac{e^{i\rho}}{\rho^{\frac{1}{2}}} \left(1 + i\frac{4p^2 - 1}{8\rho} + \cdots \right). \qquad (5.63)$$

The following fact is specially interesting; for large values of ρ the Bessel functions behave like periodic functions whose amplitude is decreasing like $1/\rho^{\frac{1}{2}}$.

Asymptotic expansions are not convergent, they are "semiconvergent", i.e., the higher terms do not decrease but increase. Nevertheless they can be used for calculations if one stops before the terms start to increase.

13. Example: heat flow with cylindrical symmetry

Assume that we have an infinitely long cylinder composed of two half cylinders each of which has a semicircular cross section. Let one of the cylinders have the temperature T, and let the other have zero temperature. Furthermore, let us assume the following law governing heat conduction through the surface to the exterior; the heat flow is proportional to the difference of temperature between the cylinder and exterior space, which is at zero temperature. We want to find the temperature u as a function of the time and of the position in the cylinder.

According to (4.7) and (3.21) the differential equation is

$$\frac{d^2u}{dr^2} + \frac{1}{r}\frac{du}{dr} + \frac{1}{r^2}\frac{d^2u}{d\varphi^2} = \frac{c\rho}{\lambda}\frac{\partial u}{\partial t}. \qquad (5.64)$$

The direction of $\varphi = 0$ is taken along the middle of the

area with temperature T. Then u will certainly be an
even function of φ. If we introduce $u = R\Phi T$, we have

$$\frac{T'}{T} = -\alpha \qquad \text{and} \qquad \frac{\Phi''}{\Phi} = -\beta$$

and hence

$$T = e^{-\alpha t} \qquad \text{and} \qquad \Phi = \cos(\beta^{\frac{1}{2}}\varphi).$$

We have not inserted any arbitrary factors here. Also,
we have not added the particular solution $\sin(\beta^{\frac{1}{2}}\varphi)$,
since it is an odd function of φ. The constant β is
determined by the condition that Φ must have the
period 2π. This corresponds to a boundary condition.
The eigenvalues are

$$\beta^{\frac{1}{2}} = n \qquad (= \text{integer}).$$

For R we now obtain the equation

$$\frac{d^2R}{dr^2} + \frac{1}{r}\frac{dR}{dr} + \left(\frac{c\rho}{\lambda}\alpha - \frac{n^2}{r^2}\right)R = 0. \qquad (5.65)$$

The solutions of this equation are Bessel functions of
order n with the argument $c\rho\alpha r/\lambda$. Since n is integer
these functions are the Bessel functions $J_n(c\rho\alpha r/\lambda)$ and
the Neumann functions $K_n(c\rho\alpha r/\lambda)$, the values and
fundamental properties of which are well known and
can be found in tables. If $r = 0$, K_n is infinite; we thus
cannot use this particular solution.

At the surface of the cylinder ($r = r_0$) we have in
addition the condition that

$$\frac{dR}{dr} + bR = 0 \qquad (b = \text{proportionality constant}).$$

From this and with $c\rho\alpha r_0/\lambda = \nu$ we obtain the transcendent equation for ν:

$$\frac{\nu}{r_0} J_n'(\nu) + bJ_n(\nu) = 0. \tag{5.66}$$

The infinitely many solutions of this equation are real. However, we are not able to prove this fact here. If we denote them by ν_m, we can write the result of our computations as

$$u = \sum_m \sum_n A_{mn} J_n\!\left(\nu_m \frac{r}{r_0}\right) \cos n\varphi$$
$$\cdot \exp\left(-\nu_m \lambda t/c\rho r_0\right) \tag{5.67}$$

The A_{mn} can be determined by means of the initial condition which states that in the region from $r = 0$ to $r = r_0$ we have, for $t = 0$,

$$u = T \qquad \text{for} \qquad -\frac{\pi}{2} < \varphi < \frac{\pi}{2}$$

and

$$u = 0 \qquad \text{for} \qquad \frac{\pi}{2} < \varphi < \frac{3}{2}\pi.$$

The general theorem (5.30) is valid here and therefore we have for $m \neq l$ and $n \neq k$ the orthogonality condition

$$\int_0^{r_0} \int_{-\pi}^{+\pi} J_n\!\left(\nu_m \frac{r}{r_0}\right) \cos n\varphi \, J_k\!\left(\nu_l \frac{r}{r_0}\right) \cos k\varphi \, r \, dr \, d\varphi = 0.$$

We must keep in mind here that the volume element is

$r\, dr\, d\varphi$ (and not $dr\, d\varphi$). Therefore we now find the coefficients A_{mn} from the equation

$$\int_0^{r_0} \int_{-\pi/2}^{+\pi/2} T J_n\!\left(\nu_m \frac{r}{r_0}\right) \cos n\varphi\, r\, dr\, d\varphi$$

$$\hspace{2cm} (5.68)$$

$$= A_{mn} \int_0^{r_0} \int_{-\pi}^{+\pi} \left\{ J_n\!\left(\nu_m \frac{r}{r_0}\right)\right\}^2 \cos^2 n\varphi\, r\, dr\, d\varphi.$$

The evaluation of these double integrals is a mere calculation which we shall not perform here.

The calculations become much simpler if there is no dependence on φ at all. This is the case when the temperature in the cylinder is constant initially. We then have $n = 0$. We only need the function J_0, for which there exist very extensive tables. The solutions of the transcendental equation can also be found in tables.

We can see in (5.67) (from the exponential function) that the terms are more highly damped the higher their order. After some time (which depends on $\lambda/c\rho r_0$), only the term with the smallest ν_m will remain.

14. Potential of a circular ring

The calculation of the potential u of a charged circular ring illustrates the use of spherical functions. (The ring may have an infinitesimal cross section.) Let the radius of the ring be a and the total charge, which is equally distributed, be M. We shall use spherical coordinates. This system may be chosen such that all points on the ring have the coordinate $\vartheta = \pi/2$. Then everything is independent of φ and the differential equation (4.1) has the form (5.40) with $\lambda = \alpha = 0$. The particular solutions are

$$R = \rho^m \quad \text{and} \quad R = \frac{1}{\rho^{m+1}}$$

$$\Theta = P_m(\cos \vartheta) \quad \text{and} \quad \Theta = Q_m(\cos \vartheta).$$

Only integral values of m are considered in the solution, because R must be unique. According to V 11 the functions P_m are algebraic of degree m in $x = \cos \vartheta$. They are even for even m and odd for odd m. Each Q_m has an infinite value for $\cos \vartheta = 1$ or $\vartheta = 0$ and thus cannot be used for our problem. We therefore try an expression of the following form

$$u = \sum_{m=0}^{\infty} A_m \rho^m P_m(\cos \vartheta) + \sum_{m=0}^{\infty} \frac{B_m}{\rho^{m+1}} P_m(\cos \vartheta). \quad (5.69)$$

In order to determine the coefficients A_m and B_m we need an inhomogeneous boundary condition. We can obtain this condition from the values of the potential on the axis $\vartheta = 0$. Each point on this axis has the same distance from all points of the ring (Fig. 36) namely $(a^2 + \rho^2)^{\frac{1}{2}}$. Each element of charge $M \, d\varphi/2\pi$ therefore produces the potential $M \, d\varphi/2\pi(a^2 + \rho^2)^{\frac{1}{2}}$. (See VII 1). The total potential for $\vartheta = 0$ is then

Fig. 36. Potential of a circular ring

$$u_0 = \frac{M}{(a^2 + \rho^2)^{\frac{1}{2}}} \quad (5.70)$$

In order to compare this expression with (5.69), we must expand it in a power series in increasing powers of (ρ/a) if $\rho < a$,

$$u_0 = \frac{M}{a}\left(1 - \frac{1}{2}\frac{\rho^2}{a^2} + \frac{1\cdot3}{2\cdot4}\frac{\rho^4}{a^4}\right.$$

$$\left. - \frac{1\cdot3\cdot5}{2\cdot4\cdot6}\frac{\rho^6}{a^6} + \cdots\right) \qquad (5.71a)$$

and in decreasing powers of (ρ/a) if $\rho > a$,

$$u_0 = M\left(\frac{1}{\rho} - \frac{1}{2}\frac{a^2}{\rho^3} + \frac{1\cdot3}{2\cdot4}\frac{a^4}{\rho^5}\right.$$

$$\left. - \frac{1\cdot3\cdot5}{2\cdot4\cdot6}\frac{a^6}{\rho^7} + \cdots\right) \qquad (5.71b)$$

For $\vartheta = 0$ all $P_m(1)$ are equal to one. By comparing (5.69) with (5.71) we find that for $\rho < a$

$$A_0 = \frac{M}{a}, \qquad A_2 = \frac{M}{a}\left(-\frac{1}{2a^2}\right) \text{ etc.,}$$

and consequently

$$= \frac{M}{a}\left\{P_0(\cos\vartheta) - \frac{1}{2}\frac{\rho^2}{a^2}P_2(\cos\vartheta)\right.$$

$$\left. + \frac{1\cdot3}{2\cdot4}\frac{\rho^4}{a^4}P_4(\cos\vartheta) - \cdots\right\}. \qquad (5.72a)$$

For $\rho > a$ we obtain

$$u = \frac{M}{a} \left\{ \frac{a}{\rho} P_0(\cos \vartheta) - \frac{1}{2} \frac{a^3}{\rho^3} P_2(\cos \vartheta) \right.$$

$$\left. + \frac{1 \cdot 3}{2 \cdot 4} \frac{a^5}{\rho^5} P_4(\cos \vartheta) - \cdots \right\}. \quad (5.72b)$$

15. Example: charged hemispheres

In order to illustrate the expansion in spherical harmonics we consider two hemispheres with radius a and the potentials $+M$ and $-M$. They are so arranged as to form a complete sphere. For the potential we again have the equation (5.40) with $\alpha = \lambda = 0$. The boundary conditions are

$$u = 0 \quad \text{for} \quad \rho = 0 \quad \text{and for} \quad \rho = \infty$$

and for $\rho = a$ we have $u = +M$ for $0 < \vartheta < \pi/2$ and $u = -M$ for $\pi/2 < \vartheta < \pi$. The solutions are again

$$u = \sum_0^\infty A_m \rho^m P_m(\cos \vartheta)$$

or

$$u = \sum_0^\infty \frac{B_m}{\rho^{m+1}} P_m(\cos \vartheta)$$

according to whether $\rho < a$ or $\rho > a$. The coefficients are again found from the inhomogeneous condition for $\rho = a$. According to the condition of orthogonality we have

$$2\pi a^2 \int_0^\pi P_m(\cos \vartheta) P_l(\cos \vartheta) \sin \vartheta \, d\vartheta = 0$$

$$\text{for} \quad m \neq l \quad (5.73)$$

and therefore

$$\int_0^{\pi/2} MP_m(\cos \vartheta) \sin \vartheta \, d\vartheta - \int_{\pi/2}^{\pi} MP_m(\cos \vartheta) \sin \vartheta \, d\vartheta$$

$$= A_m \, a^m \int_0^{\pi} (P_m(\cos \vartheta))^2 \sin \vartheta \, d\vartheta \qquad (5.74)$$

and a corresponding formula for B_m.

16. Example: propagation of waves

The properties of certain functions which are dependent on x, r, or ρ only become very clear if we compare the solutions of the equation

$$\Delta u = \frac{1}{c^2} \frac{\partial^2 u}{\partial t^2}$$

for a given time frequency ω. If Δu depends on the Cartesian coordinate x only, we obtain the equation of a plane wave

$$u = e^{\pm i\omega x/c} e^{i\omega t}, \qquad (5.75)$$

if we again use complex exponential functions for the sake of simplicity. With cylindrical symmetry we have

$$u = J_0\left(\frac{\omega}{c} r\right) e^{i\omega t}, \qquad (5.76)$$

and with spherical symmetry

$$u = \frac{e^{i\omega\rho/c}}{\rho} e^{i\omega t}. \qquad (5.77)$$

The Bessel function of order zero represents a cylindrical wave. Bessel functions of higher order represent cylindrical waves which depend on φ. The expression

$$\frac{1}{\rho} e^{i\omega\rho/c}$$

decreases like $1/\rho$ for increasing ρ. The energy of each wave pulse emitted remains constant as the wave expands. Since, however, the surface over which the energy is distributed increases like ρ^2, the amplitude must decrease like $1/\rho$ (since the energy is proportional to u^2). The energy of the cylindrical wave is distributed on a surface which increases like r. Thus the amplitude must decrease like $1/(r)^{\frac{1}{2}}$. The Bessel functions actually have this property in an asymptotic fashion, i.e., it is fulfilled more exactly the greater the value of r. This follows from (5.63). Also the subsequent zeros of the transcendent equation have asymptotically constant distances from each other like sine and cosine.

17. The Fourier integral

All of the problems which we have considered so far were concerned with a finite region. We can use the same methods for the whole space (propagation of oscillations or heat flows in the whole space). Here we must perform a limiting process which transforms the sum of the Fourier series into an integral.

For example, the function $f(x)$ may have the constant value 1 for x between $-a$ and $+a$ and the value 0 elsewhere. The process which we are considering shall not be restricted to the interval $-a$, a as it was in the case of the string. It may vary along the whole x-axis. It is not possible to work with a periodic function in this case. We must consider the function in the whole region from $-\infty$ to $+\infty$, which is the same as saying that we must give the value ∞ to the period. Since our method yields the eigenfunctions $\sin \alpha x$ and $\cos \alpha x$, we must construct the given non-periodic functions from these functions. An infinite limit for the period is equivalent to a zero limit for the frequency of the fundamental oscillation. The separated harmonic frequencies form a continuous sequence in the limit and the sum becomes an integral. The general Fourier series for a given period $-b, +b$ is

$$f(x) = \sum_{n=0}^{\infty} A_n \cos \frac{n\pi x}{b} + \sum_{n=1}^{\infty} B_n \sin \frac{n\pi x}{b},$$

with

$$A_0 = \frac{1}{2b} \int_{-b}^{+b} f(\xi)\, d\xi, \quad A_n = \frac{1}{b} \int_{-b}^{+b} f(\xi) \cos \frac{n\pi\xi}{b}\, d\xi,$$

$$B_n = \frac{1}{b} \int_{-b}^{+b} f(\xi) \sin \frac{n\pi\xi}{b}\, d\xi.$$

Here we have written ξ for the variable of integration in order to have x at our further disposal. We now change the order of integration and summation and obtain

$$f(\dot{x}) = \int_{-b}^{+b} f(\xi)\left[\frac{1}{2b} + \frac{1}{b} \sum_{n=1}^{\infty} \cos \frac{n\pi}{b}(x - \xi) \right] d\xi. \quad (5.78)$$

We put $n\pi/b = \alpha$ and keep in mind that only the large values of n have any influence if $b \to \infty$, while α goes through all values from 0 to ∞. The sum has a factor $1/b = \alpha/\pi n$ which becomes very small. In order to determine the limit, the term $1/2b$ can be neglected with respect to the sum. The sum, whose terms are infinitely small (order α/n), becomes equal to

$$\frac{1}{\pi} \int_0^\infty \cos \alpha(x - \xi) \, d\alpha,$$

if we write $d\alpha$ for α/n. We now have a representation of our arbitrary function by a Fourier integral:

$$f(x) = \frac{1}{\pi} \int_{-\infty}^{+\infty} d\xi \, f(\xi) \int_0^\infty \cos \alpha(x - \xi) \, d\alpha. \quad (5.79)$$

As an example we consider the conduction of heat in an infinitely large body whose temperature is equal to T in the strip $x = -a$ to $x = +a$ and equal to 0 at any other point at the time $t = 0$. The differential equation

$$\frac{\partial^2 u}{\partial x^2} = \frac{c\rho}{\lambda} \frac{\partial u}{\partial t}$$

has the functions $\cos \alpha x$ and $\sin \alpha x$ (and hence also $\cos \alpha(x - \xi)$) multiplied by the time factor

$$e^{-\alpha^2 \lambda t / c\rho}$$

as particular solutions. This can easily be proven by our method, or verified directly. Thus the solution for the initial temperature field $u_0 = f(x)$ is

$$u = \frac{1}{\pi} \int_{-\infty}^{+\infty} d\xi \, f(\xi) \int_0^\infty e^{-\alpha^2 \lambda t / c\rho} \cos \alpha(x - \xi) \, d\alpha. \quad (5.80)$$

In our example we have

$$f(x) = \frac{T}{\pi} \int_{-a}^{+a} d\xi \int_0^\infty \cos \alpha(x - \xi) \, d\alpha$$

and therefore

$$u = \frac{T}{\pi} \int_{-a}^{+a} d\xi \int_0^\infty e^{-\alpha^2 \lambda t / c\rho} \cos \alpha(x - \xi) \, d\alpha.$$

CHAPTER VI

SOLUTION BY CHANGE OF VARIABLES

For many differential equations we find general solutions if we use certain linear combinations of the space-time variables as new variables. This is a special case of the method of characteristics which is very important in the theory of partial differential equations. Since we shall only consider very simple cases we need not go into the general theory of characteristics.

1. Propagation of waves

The equation

$$\frac{\partial^2 u}{\partial x^2} = \frac{1}{c^2}\frac{\partial^2 u}{\partial t^2} \tag{6.1}$$

is satisfied by any function of the variables $x \pm ct$ as can be easily verified. If we set

$$u = f(x \pm ct), \tag{6.2}$$

we have

$$\frac{\partial^2 u}{\partial x^2} = f'' \quad \text{and} \quad \frac{\partial^2 u}{\partial t^2} = c^2 f'',$$

and hence (6.1).

In our case the curves having the equations $x + ct =$ const. and $x - ct =$ const. are called the characteristics. The solution

$$u = f_1(x + ct) + f_2(x - ct) \tag{6.3}$$

contains two arbitrary functions which must be determined so that the solution satisfies the boundary conditions. The function $f_1(x + ct)$ represents a wave of constant shape given by u at the time

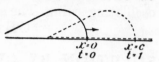

Fig. 37. Propagation of a wave

$t = 0$ moving in the direction of the negative x-axis. (Propagation of a disturbance along a rope, or a tidal wave in a canal.) In the same way $f_2(x - ct)$ represents a wave moving in the positive direction of the x-axis. If the propagation occurs in a body of infinite extent, the boundary conditions are easy to satisfy. u and $\partial u/\partial t$ must be given initially for every x. Assume

$$t = 0 : u = F(x) \qquad \frac{\partial u}{\partial t} = G(x). \qquad (6.4)$$

Then for the determination of f_1 and f_2 we have the relations.

$$f_1(x) + f_2(x) = F(x)$$
$$cf_1'(x) - cf_2'(x) = G(x).$$

With $\int G(x)\, dx = H(x)$ we obtain from these equations

$$f_1(x) = \frac{1}{2}\left[F(x) + \frac{1}{c} H(x) \right],$$

$$f_2(x) = \frac{1}{2}\left[F(x) - \frac{1}{c} H(x) \right],$$

and the complete solution of the problem is

$$u = \frac{1}{2}\left[F(x + ct) + F(x - ct) + \frac{1}{c} H(x + ct) \right.$$

$$\left. - \frac{1}{c} H(x - ct) \right]. \qquad (6.5)$$

The method can also be used if the body is finite, e.g., an oscillating string. The string (Fig. 38) may be displaced

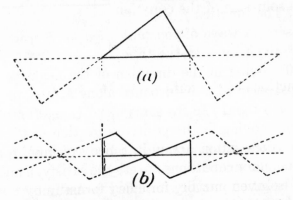

Fig. 38. Oscillation of a string as a superposition of two motions of opposite directions (*b*) from the initial state (*a*)

and then released with no acceleration (i.e., with $G(x) = 0$) at the time $t = 0$. Then we have $f_1 = f_2$, and the disturbance propagates in the same way in both directions. We can picture the oscillation of the string as due to the superpositions of two such waves travelling in opposite directions without change of shape. In order to satisfy the condition $u = 0$ at both ends we must continue the function (which is given physically for $0 \leq x \leq l$ only) in both directions so that it becomes antisymmetric and so that the disturbances propagating to the left and to the right continually cancel out one another at the points $x = 0$ and $x = l$. We say physically that the waves which arrive at those end points are reflected with a loss of half a wave length (inversion of the sign). The analogy between this extension of the functions and the Fourier series is evident.

2. Two-dimensional potential problems

The best known field of application of this method is in the solutions of the equation

$$\frac{\partial^2 \Phi}{\partial x^2} + \frac{\partial^2 \Phi}{\partial y^2} = 0 \qquad (6.6)$$

by functions of the form

$$\Phi = f_1(x + iy) + f_2(x - iy) \qquad (6.7)$$

Here i is the imaginary unit. Since Φ is real, f_1 and f_2 must be conjugate.

The solution can be simplified formally by addition of an imaginary solution $i\Psi$ which satisfies

$$\frac{\partial^2 \Psi}{\partial x^2} + \frac{\partial^2 \Psi}{\partial y^2} = 0. \qquad (6.8)$$

Furthermore Ψ shall be chosen so that the sum

$$\Phi + i\Psi = f(x + iy) \qquad (6.9)$$

is a function of the complex variable $x + iy$. We then have the Cauchy-Riemann equations relating the derivatives of Φ and Ψ:

$$\frac{\partial \Phi}{\partial x} = \frac{\partial \Psi}{\partial y},$$

$$\qquad (6.10)$$

$$\frac{\partial \Phi}{\partial y} = -\frac{\partial \Psi}{\partial x},$$

The two sides of the first of these equations represent the real part of f', those of the second, i times the imaginary part of f'.

The physical significance of these equations becomes clear, if we consider the origin of the equation (6.6) (III 10 and 11). A vector field **v**, which may represent the velocity in a potential flow or the force in a static field, satisfies the equations

$$\text{curl } \mathbf{v} = 0 \qquad (6.11)$$

and

$$\text{div } \mathbf{v} = 0. \qquad (6.12)$$

In addition we have the independence of the z-coordinate. We have previously introduced a scalar potential $\mathbf{v} = \text{grad } \Phi$ because of (6.11), and this potential function must satisfy $\Delta\Phi = 0$ (because of (6.12)).

In the same way we can introduce a vector potential according to (6.12), for which $\Delta\Psi = 0$ from (6.11). In this case of a plane problem, the vector potential only has one component and is therefore a scalar like Φ for the purposes of our computations.

3. Lines of constant potential and stream lines

The components u and v of the vector **v** are

$$u = \frac{\partial\Phi}{\partial x} = \frac{\partial\Psi}{\partial y'} \qquad v = \frac{\partial\Phi}{\partial y} = -\frac{\partial\Psi}{\partial x} \qquad (6.13)$$

The curves $\Phi = $ const. (curves of constant potential) are given by

$$\frac{\partial\Phi}{\partial x}\, dx + \frac{\partial\Phi}{\partial y}\, dy = 0$$

or

$$\frac{dy}{dx} = -\frac{u}{v}. \qquad (6.14)$$

Similarly we have for the curves Ψ = const.

$$\frac{dy}{dx} = \frac{v}{u}. \tag{6.15}$$

This means that the direction of these curves is the same as the direction of the vector **v**. The curves have the direction of the field vector at every point in the field. For this reason these curves are called stream lines or lines of force (according to the nature of the problem). Equations (6.14) and (6.15) show that stream lines and the lines of constant potential are perpendicular to each other at every point.

By sketching this network of lines we may obtain a clear picture of the whole process. The direction of the field vector at any point is given by the direction of the stream line in this sketch. We can also find the length of the vector by the following consideration. Let us give to the constants in Φ = const. and Ψ = const. a sequence of values having a constant difference ϵ which is sufficiently small. Now if we choose the coordinate system at any point such that the direction of the x-axis is the direction of the stream line and the direction of the y-axis that of the line of constant potential (Fig. 39), then the distance

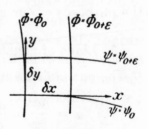

Fig. 39. Element of a net of potential and stream lines

δx between the two equipotential lines whose difference of potential is ϵ satisfies

$$\frac{\partial \Phi}{\partial x}\, \delta x = \epsilon.$$

The distance δy of two stream lines with Ψ-difference of ϵ satisfies

$$\frac{\partial \Psi}{\partial y} \, \delta y = \epsilon.$$

Thus according to (6.10) we have $\delta x = \delta y$ and the net is composed of small squares. Keeping ϵ fixed, the squares of this net are smaller the greater the absolute value of the field vector $\mathbf{v}$, since the latter is equal to $\partial \Phi / \partial x$. As an illustration we shall later show the representation of a potential flow and of the electric potential in a condenser.

In order to obtain such solutions we still must learn how to satisfy the boundary conditions. They can also be expressed in terms of Φ and Ψ in the simplest cases. In the case of the flow of a fluid, for example, the surface of any rigid body must be a stream line (Ψ = const.) since the direction of flow must be tangential to the surface. In electrostatic problems, the lines of force are always normal to a conducting surface, along which the potential is constant. (Φ = const.). The two cases are equivalent from the mathematical standpoint. If

$$w = \Phi + i\Psi$$

and

$$z = x + iy,$$

we have the complex equation

$$w = f(z) \tag{6.16}$$

It is easy to find the function f in certain simple cases. For example, if the potential flow has a constant velocity U parallel to the x-axis we have

$$w = Uz, \qquad (6.17)$$

and by differentiation we find

$$u = \frac{\partial \Phi}{\partial x} = U \qquad \text{and} \qquad v = \frac{\partial \Phi}{\partial y} = 0$$

The electrostatic field produced by a condenser which consists of two infinite planes at $y = 0$ and $y = a$ having the potentials 0 and Φ_0, respectively, is

$$w = -iz\Phi_0/a \qquad (6.18)$$

This means that $\Phi = \Phi_0 y/a$ and thus satisfies the boundary condition. All the lines of force $\Psi = -\Phi_0 x/a$ are normal to the plates.

4. Conformal mapping

Difficult cases, like the flow around a cylinder (Fig. 40), are treated by the following method. One introduces the new variable $\zeta = \xi + i\eta$ and tries to find a function $z = \varphi(\zeta)$ which establishes a correspondence between the boundary values ζ of the difficult problem with the boundary values z of a simple problem whose solution is known. For example, we may try to establish a correspondence between the central stream line of the simple parallel flow (6.17) and the stream line which curves around the cylinder.

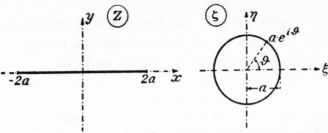

Fig. 40. Conformal mapping of a twice traversed segment onto a circle

If then $f(z)$ is the solution of the simple problem, the function

$$w = f[\varphi(\zeta)] = f_1(\zeta) \qquad (6.19)$$

is the solution of the difficult problem. For every (analytic) function of a complex variable is a solution according to our fundamental idea. In addition, this solution satisfies the boundary condition and is therefore the solution we are looking for.

The variables x and y have been replaced by the variables ξ, η through the equation $z = \varphi(\zeta)$. This is usually expressed by saying that we have mapped the complex z-plane onto the complex ζ-plane. This mapping transforms the solution for the simple case of the variables x and y into the solution of the more difficult case as described by the variables ξ and η. For our example (parallel flow $\rightarrow$ flow around cylinder) we can use the function

$$z = \zeta + \frac{a^2}{\zeta} \qquad (6.20)$$

For if $\zeta = ae^{i\vartheta}$ (which is a point on the circle), the corresponding z is real and equal to $2a \cos \vartheta$. This is a point on the x-axis between $-2a$ and $+2a$. All real values of ζ are also mapped into real values of z. Thus the x-axis of the z-plane is mapped onto the ξ-axis plus the circle of the ζ-plane. In both cases this is a stream line ($\Psi = 0$). Each stream line in the z-plane is transformed into a stream line of the ζ-plane by the same mapping, and the same is true for the lines of constant potential. This can be calculated by introducing (6.20) in (6.17)

$$w = U\left(\zeta + \frac{a^2}{\zeta}\right). \tag{6.21}$$

From this we obtain

$$\Phi + i\Psi = U\left(x + iy + \frac{a^2}{x + iy}\right)$$

or

$$\Phi = U\left(x + \frac{a^2 x}{x^2 + y^2}\right) \text{ and } \Psi = U\left(y - \frac{a^2 y}{x^2 + y^2}\right)$$

The result is represented in Fig. 42.

This method and the properties of conformal mapping are a subject of major interest in the theory of functions. One of the most important properties is the invariance of the angle between any two directions under a conformal mapping, except at singular points. This means, in particular, that the stream lines and

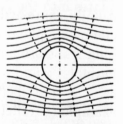

Fig. 41. Flow around a cylinder
——Ψ = const.,
$\cdots$ Φ = const.

lines of constant potential remain normal if a conformal mapping is applied to them.

5. Examples

For many cases the mapping functions are completely known. There also exist general theorems concerning the mapping of a polygon onto a half plane or a circle, etc. However, we cannot consider special questions here. The example of the flow around a circle is of particular importance because it is possible to map the circle into the contour of an airfoil. As another illustration we shall use the example of a condenser by mapping from the trivial case (6.18). The mapping

$$z = \frac{a}{\pi} \log \zeta \tag{6.22}$$

maps every real z into a positive real ζ. Since

$$\log (-r) = i\pi + \log r,$$

there corresponds a negative real ζ to every point on the line $z = x + ia$ which represents one of the condenser plates in (6.18). Thus (6.22) maps the two plates into the two parts of the ζ-axis and the equation

$$w = -i \frac{\Phi_0}{\pi} \log \zeta \tag{6.23}$$

describes the electrostatic field produced by two parallel plates at different potentials. By separation of the real and the imaginary part in (6.23) we find

$$\Phi + i\Psi = -i \frac{\Phi_0}{\pi} \log (re^{i\vartheta}) = -i \frac{\Phi_0}{\pi} (\log r + i\vartheta)$$

$$= -i \frac{\Phi_0}{\pi} \log r + \frac{\Phi_0}{\pi} \vartheta.$$

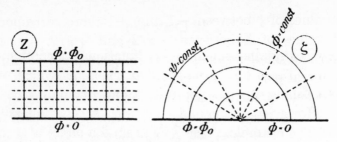

Fig. 42. Mapping of a strip into a half-plane

The lines of constant potential are the lines through the origin (ϑ = const.) and the lines of force are the circles with the origin as center (r = const.). We shall now apply another mapping to the ζ-plane transforming it into the Z-plane by the function

$$Z = \text{arc sin } \zeta \quad \text{or} \quad \zeta = \sin Z. \quad (6.24)$$

The real axis of the ζ-plane is then transformed into the contour of the Z-plane which is shown in Fig. 43. To

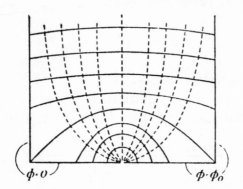

Fig. 43. Example of a conformal mapping
— Ψ = const., $\cdots$ Φ = const.

the values of ζ between -1 and $+1$ there correspond real values of Z between $-\pi/2$ and $+\pi/2$. To the larger and smaller values of ζ there correspond Z-values whose real part is $-\pi/2$ or $+\pi/2$.

The field quantities are contained in the equation

$$w = -i\frac{\Phi_0}{\pi} \log \sin Z \qquad (6.25)$$

and numerical calculation gives the curves of Fig. 43.

CHAPTER VII

SOLUTION BY THE USE OF SINGULARITIES

It is often easy to find the solution of a differential equation which is defined in all space and is equal to zero at points at infinity, but which has a singularity at one point, i.e., becomes infinite at this point. Whether or not this function has a physical meaning depends on the nature of the singularity.

1. Source

The clearest example of the above is the potential flow produced by a source. The differential equation

$$\Delta\Phi = 0 \tag{7.1}$$

must be valid in the whole space, but at the origin where there is a source. The equation cannot be valid there, for according to (4.15) it expresses the fact that there is no source in the region of its validity. The solution evidently has spherical symmetry with the point of origin as center and is therefore a function of the radius only. From the form (3.22) of the differential equation

$$\frac{d}{d\rho}\left(\rho^2 \frac{d\Phi}{d\rho}\right) = 0, \tag{7.2}$$

we obtain the two particular solutions $\Phi = \text{const.}/\rho$ and $\Phi = \text{const.}$ The latter has no physical meaning. The former is equal to zero at infinity and has a singularity at the origin. It is therefore the representation of the source flow we seek. The constant depends on the magnitude of the source. If we write $\Phi = -C/\rho$, the vector **v** which is free of sources in the whole space except at the origin has the magnitude

$$v = \frac{d\Phi}{d\rho} = +\frac{C}{\rho^2}.$$

For the integral of the divergence of **v** over any sphere which encloses the origin we obtain, with the use of the theorem of Gauss (3.12),

$$Q = \int \text{div } \mathbf{v} \, dV = \int \frac{C}{\rho_0^2} \rho_0^2 \, d\omega, \qquad (7.3)$$

where $d\omega$ is the element of the solid angle and ρ_0 is the radius of the sphere. We find

$$Q = 4\pi C. \qquad (7.4)$$

The quantity of fluid leaving the sphere in unit time must be independent of the radius of the sphere, since otherwise the region between two spheres would not be free of sources. The solution of (7.2) is

$$\Phi = -\frac{Q}{4\pi\rho}. \qquad (7.5)$$

This is the mathematical expression for a point source. The result is the same for the potential in the gravitation field of a single mass point, since the differential equation is the same (4.3). To the constant Q there corresponds the number $-4\pi f M$, if f is the constant of gravitation and M the mass of the point. By differentiation with respect to ρ we obtain Newton's law that the force per unit mass is $-fM/r^2$.

2. Superposition of positive and negative sources

By summation of such fundamental solutions we can find solutions of more complicated cases, since the equation is linear and homogeneous. In this way we find the potential of a continuous distribution of sources whose strength per unit volume is a function μ of position,

$$
\Phi = - \int \frac{\mu dV}{4\pi\rho}
$$

$$
= - \int \frac{\mu(\xi, \eta, \zeta)}{4\pi\rho(\xi, \eta, \zeta; x, y, z)} \, d\xi \, d\eta \, d\zeta .
$$

(7.6)

This is a solution of the differential equation

$$
\Delta\Phi = \mu,
$$

(7.7)

since $\Delta\Phi = \text{div } \mathbf{v}$ is the strength per unit volume. In order to calculate the integral (7.6) we must remember that the origin of ρ depends on the point here. If the potential at the point x, y, z is to be calculated, for example, we have in the integrand

$$
\rho = [(x - \xi)^2 + (y - \eta)^2 + (z - \zeta)^2]^{\frac{1}{2}} .
$$

(7.8)

μ can also have negative values. A particularly important case is the one where a positive and a negative source (for example electric charges) of equal magnitude are very close together. This is called a dipole (Fig. 44). If the distance ρ from the dipole is large compared with the length ϵ of the dipole, the potential can be written in the following way

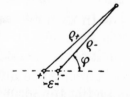

Fig. 44. Dipole

$$\Phi = \frac{Q}{4\pi}\left(\frac{1}{\rho_+} - \frac{1}{\rho_-}\right) = + \frac{Q\epsilon \cos\varphi}{4\pi\rho^2}. \qquad (7.9)$$

$Q\epsilon$ is called moment of the dipole.

3. Satisfying the boundary conditions

Simple boundary conditions can also be satisfied with our fundamental solutions if we use the method of reflection. If, for example, we have a source and a wall on which the normal component must be zero (potential flow), then we introduce an ideal source of the same magnitude whose position is symmetrical to the first source with respect to the wall. If on the other hand the wall has a constant potential (electric potential), the second source must be assumed to have the same magnitude but opposite sign (Fig. 45).

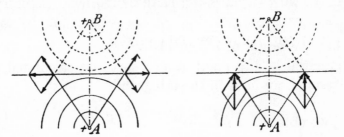

Fig. 45. Reflections

In the first case the field is

$$\Phi = \frac{Q}{4\pi\rho_A} + \frac{Q}{4\pi\rho_B}, \qquad (7.10)$$

and in the second case it is

$$\Phi = \frac{Q}{4\pi\rho_A} - \frac{Q}{4\pi\rho_B}. \qquad (7.11)$$

The boundary conditions can be satisfied for other than plane walls by superposition of negative and positive sources and dipoles. By superposition of a parallel flow along the x-axis and a dipole at the origin we obtain, for example,

$$\Phi = Ux + \frac{Q\epsilon \cos \varphi}{4\pi\rho^2} = \left(U\rho + \frac{Q\epsilon}{4\pi\rho^2} \right) \cos \varphi \quad (7.12)$$

If we calculate the component $\partial\Phi/\partial\rho$ (the radial component of the velocity) on the sphere with radius $\rho_0 = (Q\epsilon/2\pi U)^{\frac{1}{3}}$, we obtain zero. Thus (7.12) represents a potential flow around a sphere. By point sources or a continuous distribution of sources along the x-axis, we obtain bodies of revolution (other than the sphere) for which the potential flow can be easily calculated.

If the flow is plane, we have cylindrical symmetry. In this case the potential of the source can be calculated from the differential equation

$$\frac{d}{dr}\left(r \frac{d\Phi}{dr} \right) = 0$$

and we obtain

$$\Phi = \frac{Q}{2\pi} \log r. \quad (7.13)$$

The corresponding dipole potential is

$$\Phi = \frac{Q\epsilon \cos \varphi}{2\pi r}.$$

We obtain the flow around a circular cylinder by superposition of this dipole with a parallel flow

$$\Phi = Ux + \frac{Q}{2\pi} \frac{\cos \varphi}{r}, \tag{7.13a}$$

With $Q/2\pi a^2 = U$ we again obtain formula (6.21).

4. Solutions with the aid of the theorem of Green

From Green's theorem (5.27) we obtain a general and physically clear solution of $\Delta\Phi = \mu$, if we introduce $\Psi = 1/\rho$. As origin for the coordinate ρ we take the point at which we want to know the potential. Since $\Delta(1/\rho) = 0$, we obtain

$$\int \Delta\Phi \frac{1}{\rho} dV = \int \left(\frac{1}{\rho} \frac{\partial\Phi}{\partial n} - \Phi \frac{\partial}{\partial n}\left(\frac{1}{\rho}\right) \right) df. \tag{7.14}$$

We shall apply this equation to a region whose exterior is arbitrarily limited or unlimited, but from which we have cut out a small sphere of radius ρ_0 whose center is at $\rho = 0$. On this sphere we have

$$\frac{\partial}{\partial n}\left(\frac{1}{\rho}\right) = +\frac{1}{\rho^2}$$

(n is the *outward* normal, i.e., in this case the direction toward the point of origin!). Furthermore we have $df = \rho^2 \, d\omega$ ($d\omega$ = solid angle). If we now take the limit $\rho_0 \rightarrow 0$, the first term of the integral on the right side of (7.14) cancels out and the second becomes equal to $-4\pi\Phi_0$, if Φ_0 is the potential at the origin which we are looking for. Thus we have

$$4\pi\Phi_0 = -\int \Delta\Phi \frac{1}{\rho} dV + \int \frac{1}{\rho} \frac{\partial\Phi}{\partial n} df$$

$$-\int \Phi \frac{\partial}{\partial n}\left(\frac{1}{\rho}\right) df, \tag{7.15}$$

where we must now integrate only over the exterior surface of the region.

The three terms on the right hand side of (7.15) have a special physical meaning. The space integral, which is the same as (7.6), represents the potential of the charges or masses. The surface integrals show the influence of the boundary values. $\partial\Phi/\partial n$ is the normal component of the vector grad Φ at the boundary and thus is equal to the intensity of the field vector which enters the region V through the surface f. If the region is

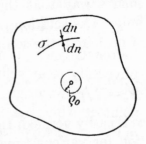

Fig. 46. Charge on a surface and on a point

limited by a metallic cover $\partial\Phi/\partial n$ can be considered as "surface charge" according to (4.34).

For an interpretation of the last integral in (7.15) we shall consider a region of infinitesimal thickness, which in the limit is "bounded by the two sides of a surface". On both sides of this region, $\partial(1/\rho)/\partial n$ has the same magnitude but opposite signs. If, therefore, Φ is the same on both sides, the integral is equal to zero. It is finite if the potential is not continuous through the surface. Such a discontinuity is caused by a distribution of dipoles (opposite charges on both sides of the surface).

5. Heat source

This method is also useful in the theory of the conduction of heat. We shall consider a one-dimensional region in which the differential equation

$$\frac{\partial^2 u}{\partial x^2} = \frac{1}{k}\frac{\partial u}{\partial t} \qquad (7.16)$$

is valid. Let us assume that at the point $x = 0$ there is a "heat source". This means that at the instant $t = 0$ the temperature at this point becomes infinite, but in such a way that the total quantity of heat remains finite. The solution of (7.17), which describes the flow of heat from the source is then

$$u = \frac{1}{(4\pi kt)^{\frac{1}{2}}} e^{-x^2/4kt}, \tag{7.17}$$

as is easily verified. In Fig. 47 we have drawn this function for various times. By the use of reflections it is also possible to satisfy the most important boundary

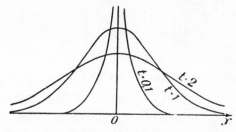

Fig. 47. The flow of heat from a heat source

conditions in this case. An arbitrary initial temperature $f(x)$ can be considered as the sum of heat sources of strength $f(\xi)\, d\xi$ at the points $x = \xi$ and produces a solution in the form of an integral

$$u = \frac{1}{(4\pi kt)^{\frac{1}{2}}} \int_{-\infty}^{+\infty} f(\xi) e^{-(x-\xi)^2/4kt}\, d\xi. \tag{7.18}$$

This formula is equivalent to the formula (5.80) which we obtained from the Fourier integral, since

$$\int_0^\infty e^{-\alpha^2 kt} \cos \alpha(x - \xi)\, d\alpha = \left(\frac{\pi}{4kt}\right)^{\frac{1}{2}} e^{-(x-\xi)^2/4kt}.$$

This formula, however, cannot be proved here. In the two-dimensional case, (7.17) is replaced by

$$u = \frac{1}{4\pi kt} e^{-r^2/4kt} \tag{7.19}$$

and in the three-dimensional by

$$u = \frac{1}{(4\pi kt)^{3/2}} e^{-\rho^2/4kt}. \tag{7.20}$$

6. Flash of light

We can also find a solution containing a singularity for the wave equation. A light flash which is emitted from the origin at the instant $t = 0$ obeys the differential equation

$$\frac{1}{\rho^2} \frac{\partial}{\partial \rho} \left(\rho^2 \frac{\partial u}{\partial \rho} \right) = \frac{1}{c^2} \frac{\partial^2 u}{dt^2} \tag{7.21}$$

in spherical coordinates. A solution of this equation is

$$u = \frac{C}{\rho} F(\rho - ct) \tag{7.22}$$

as can be easily verified.

Now let $F(x)$ be the "delta" function which is equal to zero everywhere except at $x = 0$. At this point the function is infinite in such a way that

$$\int_{-\infty}^{+\infty} F(x)\, dx = 1. \tag{7.23}$$

(For a more exact theory, we should consider a sequence of functions which have the formulated properties in the limit). The constant C is determined by the magnitude Q of the flash. We obtain the relation by calculating the flow from a region with the small radius ρ_0 and the point of origin as center (df = surface element)

$$Q = \int_0^\infty dt \int \frac{\partial u}{\partial \rho}\, df = -\int_0^\infty 4\pi \rho_0^2 \frac{C}{\rho_0^2} F(\rho_0 - ct)\, dt,$$

since

$$\frac{\partial u}{\partial \rho} = -\frac{C}{\rho^2} F + \frac{C}{\rho} F'$$

and since the second term with $\rho_0 \to 0$ becomes equal to zero on integration. According to (7.23) we now have

$$Q = \frac{4\pi C}{c}. \tag{7.24}$$

This representation is of special importance in electronic theory. There we have the equation (7.21) for the scalar potential and the three components of the vector potential in empty space, according to (4.31). At the distance ρ from the point where we seek the scalar potential Φ, there may now be a volume element dV which at the time $t = \tau$ contains the charge $\mu\, dV$ during the time $d\tau$. According to (7.22) and (7.24) we have

$$d\Phi = \frac{c}{4\pi} \mu\, dV \frac{1}{\rho} F[\rho - c(t - \tau)]\, d\tau. \tag{7.25}$$

We obtain the total potential by integrating over the whole space and all time elements from $-\infty$ to $+\infty$.

$$4\pi\Phi = \int \frac{dV}{\rho}\, \mu^*. \qquad (7.26)$$

Here μ^* is the charge density in the volume element dV at the time $t - \tau = \rho/c$. This instant is earlier than the time t at which we want to know the potential. The difference of time is ρ/c, which is just the time required by the impulse to travel the distance ρ. That is why the integrand in (7.26) and the corresponding expressions for **A** are called the retarded potentials.

7. Transition to integral equations

The solutions which we obtained by the method of singularities are expressed by an integral, the domain of which is the whole domain of an auxiliary variable. The typical form is clearly illustrated in the example (7.18), which contains only one variable

$$u(x,\, t) = \int_{-\infty}^{+\infty} f(\xi)K(x - \xi,\, t)\, d\xi. \qquad (7.27)$$

The function K is a solution of the equation which has a singularity at $x = \xi$. The dependence on t is of no importance in evaluating the integral. The elementary process with the singularity at $x = \xi$ is described by the function K. Here we need no longer bother about the deduction of K from the differential equation.

It may be that the function $f(x)$ is not given initially. The function $u(x)$ might be given instead (for a certain t), and then the problem is to determine $f(x)$. In this case $f(x)$ is the unknown in the equation (7.27) which is an *integral equation of the first type*. K is called the kernel of the equation.

The problem of finding the initial heat sources from the heat function at a certain instant seldom occurs in practice. However, problems of this kind occur frequently in other fields. If, for example, one has to determine the flow around an airship of a certain shape, one uses an integral equation similar to (7.6) in

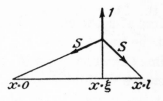

Fig. 48. String, stretched by a single force

order to calculate the sources which can generate the flow according to VII 12 from the given form of the stream lines.

The representation by an integral equation becomes even more important if u itself is unknown, while there exists a known relation between u and $f(\xi)$. We have such a case in the example of the oscillating string. The oscillation is caused by the equilibrium between the forces of inertia and the tension. In order to find a fundamental solution we consider a string which is deplaced by a single unit force (see Fig. 48). If u is the displacement and S the tension, then we have the equations

$$K(x, \xi) = \frac{1}{Sl} x(l - \xi) \qquad \text{for} \qquad x < \xi$$

$$\text{(7.28)}$$

$$K(x, \xi) = \frac{1}{Sl} \xi(1 - x) \qquad \text{for} \qquad x > \xi.$$

This function $K(x, \xi)$ is the kernel of the integral equation. The force of inertia at the point ξ corresponds to the function $f(\xi)$. If the oscillation is

$$u = y(\xi) \sin \nu t, \tag{7.29}$$

this force is $\rho \nu^2 y(\xi) \, d\xi \sin \nu t$. Thus we obtain the integral equation

$$y(x) = \rho \nu^2 \int_0^l y(\xi) K(x, \xi) \, d\xi, \tag{7.30}$$

which is a so-called *homogeneous integral equation of the second type*. If, on the left hand side, we have an additional known function of x besides $y(x)$, the equation is inhomogeneous and of the second kind. The parameter ν has here the same properties as an eigenvalue in the case of differential equations. In our examples, the same problem can be expressed by a differential equation with boundary conditions or by an integral equation. The boundary conditions are automatically satisfied by the form of the kernel in the latter case.

Index

Catalogue of Dover
SCIENCE BOOKS

BOOKS THAT EXPLAIN SCIENCE

THE NATURE OF LIGHT AND COLOUR IN THE OPEN AIR, M. Minnaert. Why is falling snow sometimes black? What causes mirages, the fata morgana, multiple suns and moons in the sky; how are shadows formed? Prof. Minnaert of U. of Utrecht answers these and similar questions in optics, light, colour, for non-specialists. Particularly valuable to nature, science students, painters, photographers. "Can best be described in one word—fascinating!" Physics Today. Translated by H. M. Kremer-Priest, K. Jay. 202 illustrations, including 42 photos. xvi + 362pp. 5⅜ x 8.　　　　　　　　　　　　　　　　　　T196 Paperbound **$1.95**

THE RESTLESS UNIVERSE, Max Born. New enlarged version of this remarkably readable account by a Nobel laureate. Moving from sub-atomic particles to universe, the author explains in very simple terms the latest theories of wave mechanics. Partial contents: air and its relatives, electrons and ions, waves and particles, electronic structure of the atom, nuclear physics. Nearly 1000 illustrations, including 7 animated sequences. 325pp. 6 x 9.　　　　　　　　　　　　　　　　　　　　　　　　　T412 Paperbound **$2.00**

MATTER AND LIGHT, THE NEW PHYSICS, L. de Broglie. Non-technical papers by a Nobel laureate explain electromagnetic theory, relativity, matter, light, radiation, wave mechanics, quantum physics, philosophy of science. Einstein, Planck, Bohr, others explained so easily that no mathematical training is needed for all but 2 of the 21 chapters. "Easy simplicity and lucidity . . . should make this source-book of modern physcis available to a wide public," Saturday Review. Unabridged. 300pp. 5⅜ x 8.　　　　　T35 Paperbound **$1.60**

THE COMMON SENSE OF THE EXACT SCIENCES, W. K. Clifford. Introduction by James Newman, edited by Karl Pearson. For 70 years this has been a guide to classical scientific, mathematical thought. Explains with unusual clarity basic concepts such as extension of meaning of symbols, characteristics of surface boundaries, properties of plane figures, vectors, Cartesian method of determining position, etc. Long preface by Bertrand Russell. Bibliography of Clifford. Corrected. 130 diagrams redrawn. 249pp. 5⅜ x 8.
　　　　　　　　　　　　　　　　　　　　　　　　　　　T61 Paperbound **$1.60**

THE EVOLUTION OF SCIENTIFIC THOUGHT FROM NEWTON TO EINSTEIN, A. d'Abro. Einstein's special, general theories of relativity, with historical implications, analyzed in non-technical terms. Excellent accounts of contributions of Newton, Riemann, Weyl, Planck, Eddington, Maxwell, Lorentz, etc., are treated in terms of space, time, equations of electromagnetics, finiteness of universe, methodology of science. "Has become a standard work," Nature. 21 diagrams. 482pp. 5⅜ x 8.　　　　　　　　　　　　　　　T2 Paperbound **$2.00**

BRIDGES AND THEIR BUILDERS, D. Steinman, S. R. Watson. Engineers, historians, everyone ever fascinated by great spans will find this an endless source of information and interest. Dr. Steinman, recent recipient of Louis Levy Medal, is one of the great bridge architects, engineers of all time. His analysis of great bridges of history is both authoritative and easily followed. Greek, Roman, medieval, oriental bridges; modern works such as Brooklyn Bridge, Golden Gate Bridge, etc. described in terms of history, constructional principles, artistry, function. Most comprehensive, accurate semi-popular history of bridges in print in English. New, greatly revised, enlarged edition. 23 photographs, 26 line drawings. xvii + 401pp. 5⅜ x 8.　　　　　　　　　　　　　　　　　　T431 Paperbound **$1.95**

CONCERNING THE NATURE OF THINGS, Sir William Bragg. Christmas lectures at Royal Society by Nobel laureate, dealing with atoms, gases, liquids, and various types of crystals. No scientific background is needed to understand this remarkably clear introduction to basic processes and aspects of modern science. "More interesting than any bestseller," London Morning Post. 32pp. of photos. 57 figures. xii + 232pp. 5⅜ x 8. T31 Paperbound **$1.35**

THE RISE OF THE NEW PHYSICS, A. d'Abro. Half million word exposition, formerly titled "The Decline of Mechanism," for readers not versed in higher mathematics. Only thorough explanation in everyday language of core of modern mathematical physical theory, treating both classical, modern views. Scientifically impeccable coverage of thought from Newtonian system through theories of Dirac, Heisenberg, Fermi's statistics. Combines history, exposition; broad but unified, detailed view, with constant comparison of classical, modern views. "A must for anyone doing serious study in the physical sciences," J. of the Franklin Inst. "Extraordinary faculty . . . to explain ideas and theories . . . in language of everyday life," Isis. Part I of set: philosophy of science, from practice of Newton, Maxwell, Poincaré, Einstein, etc. Modes of thought, experiment, causality, etc. Part II: 100 pp. on grammar, vocabulary of mathematics, discussions of functions, groups, series, Fourier series, etc. Remainder treats concrete, detailed coverage of both classical, quantum physics: analytic mechanics, Hamilton's principle, electromagnetic waves, thermodynamics, Brownian movement, special relativity, Bohr's atom, de Broglie's wave mechanics, Heisenberg's uncertainty, scores of other important topics. Covers discoveries, theories of d'Alembert, Born, Cantor, Debye, Euler, Foucault, Galois, Gauss, Hadamard, Kelvin, Kepler Laplace, Maxwell, Pauli, Rayleigh Volterra, Weyl, more than 180 others. 97 illustrations. ix + 982pp. 5⅜ x 8.
T3 Vol. 1 Paperbound **$2.00**
T4 Vol. II Paperbound **$2.00**

SPINNING TOPS AND GYROSCOPIC MOTION, John Perry. Well-known classic of science still unsurpassed for lucid, accurate, delightful exposition. How quasi-rigidity is induced in flexible, fluid bodies by rapid motions; why gyrostat falls, top rises; nature, effect of internal fluidity on rotating bodies; etc. Appendixes describe practical use of gyroscopes in ships, compasses, monorail transportation. 62 figures. 128pp. 5⅜ x 8.
T416 Paperbound **$1.00**

FOUNDATIONS OF PHYSICS, R. B. Lindsay, H. Margenau. Excellent bridge between semi-popular and technical writings. Discussion of methods of physical description, construction of theory; valuable to physicist with elementary calculus. Gives meaning to data, tools of modern physics. Contents: symbolism, mathematical equations; space and time; foundations of mechanics; probability; physics, continua; electron theory; relativity; quantum mechanics; causality; etc. "Thorough and yet not overdetailed. Unreservedly recommended," Nature. Unabridged corrected edition. 35 illustrations. xi + 537pp. 5⅜ x 8. S377 Paperbound **$2.45**

FADS AND FALLACIES IN THE NAME OF SCIENCE, Martin Gardner. Formerly entitled "In the Name of Science," the standard account of various cults, quack systems, delusions which have masqueraded as science: hollow earth fanatics, orgone sex energy, dianetics, Atlantis, Forteanism, flying saucers, medical fallacies like zone therapy, etc. New chapter on Bridey Murphy, psionics, other recent manifestations. A fair reasoned appraisal of eccentric theory which provides excellent innoculation. "Should be read by everyone, scientist or non-scientist alike," R. T. Birge, Prof. Emeritus of Physics, Univ. of Calif; Former Pres., Amer. Physical Soc. x + 365pp. 5⅜ x 8. T394 Paperbound **$1.50**

ON MATHEMATICS AND MATHEMATICIANS, R. E. Moritz. A 10 year labor of love by discerning, discriminating Prof. Moritz, this collection conveys the full sense of mathematics and personalities of great mathematicians. Anecdotes, aphorisms, reminiscences, philosophies, definitions, speculations, biographical insights, etc. by great mathematicians, writers: Descartes, Mill, Locke, Kant, Coleridge, Whitehead, etc. Glimpses into lives of great mathematicians, from Archimedes to Euler, Gauss, Weierstrass. To mathematicians, a superb browsing-book. To laymen, exciting revelation of fullness of mathematics. Extensive cross index. 410pp. 5⅜ x 8. T489 Paperbound **$1.95**

GUIDE TO THE LITERATURE OF MATHEMATICS AND PHYSICS, N. G. Parke III. Over 5000 entries under approximately 120 major subject headings, of selected most important books, monographs, periodicals, articles in English, plus important works in German, French, Italian, Spanish, Russian. (many recently available works). Covers every branch of physics, math, related engineering. Includes author, title, edition, publisher, place, date, number of volumes, number of pages. 40 page introduction on basic problems of research, study provides useful information on organization, use of libraries, psychology of learning, etc. Will save you hours of time. 2nd revised edition. Indices of authors, subjects. 464pp. 5⅜ x 8. S447 Paperbound **$2.49**

THE STRANGE STORY OF THE QUANTUM, An Account for the General Reader of the Growth of Ideas Underlying Our Present Atomic Knowledge, B. Hoffmann. Presents lucidly, expertly, with barest amount of mathematics, problems and theories which led to modern quantum physics. Begins with late 1800's when discrepancies were noticed; with illuminating analogies, examples, goes through concepts of Planck, Einstein, Pauli, Schroedinger, Dirac, Sommerfield, Feynman, etc. New postscript through 1958. "Of the books attempting an account of the history and contents of modern atomic physics which have come to my attention, this is the best," H. Margenau, Yale U., in Amer. J. of Physics. 2nd edition. 32 tables, illustrations. 275pp. 5⅜ x 8. T518 Paperbound **$1.45**

2

HISTORY OF SCIENCE
AND PHILOSOPHY OF SCIENCE

THE VALUE OF SCIENCE, Henri Poincaré. Many of most mature ideas of "last scientific universalist" for both beginning, advanced workers. Nature of scientific truth, whether order is innate in universe or imposed by man, logical thought vs. intuition (relating to Weierstrass, Lie, Riemann, etc), time and space (relativity, psychological time, simultaneity), Herz's concept of force, values within disciplines of Maxwell, Carnot, Mayer, Newton, Lorentz, etc. iii + 147pp. 5⅜ x 8.
S469 Paperbound **$1.35**

PHILOSOPHY AND THE PHYSICISTS, L. S. Stebbing. Philosophical aspects of modern science examined in terms of lively critical attack on ideas of Jeans, Eddington. Tasks of science, causality, determinism, probability, relation of world physics to that of everyday experience, philosophical significance of Planck-Bohr concept of discontinuous energy levels, inferences to be drawn from Uncertainty Principle, implications of "becoming" involved in 2nd law of thermodynamics, other problems posed by discarding of Laplacean determinism. 285pp. 5⅜ x 8.
T480 Paperbound **$1.65**

THE PRINCIPLES OF SCIENCE, A TREATISE ON LOGIC AND THE SCIENTIFIC METHOD, W. S. Jevons. Milestone in development of symbolic logic remains stimulating contribution to investigation of inferential validity in sciences. Treats inductive, deductive logic, theory of number, probability, limits of scientific method; significantly advances Boole's logic, contains detailed introduction to nature and methods of probability in physics, astronomy, everyday affairs, etc. In introduction, Ernest Nagel of Columbia U. says,"[Jevons] continues to be of interest as an attempt to articulate the logic of scientific inquiry." liii + 786pp. 5⅜ x 8.
S446 Paperbound **$2.98**

A HISTORY OF ASTRONOMY FROM THALES TO KEPLER, J. L. E. Dreyer. Only work in English to give complete history of cosmological views from prehistoric times to Kepler. Partial contents: Near Eastern astronomical systems, Early Greeks, Homocentric spheres of Euxodus, Epicycles, Ptolemaic system, Medieval cosmology, Copernicus, Kepler, much more. "Especially useful to teachers and students of the history of science . . . unsurpassed in its field," Isis. Formerly "A History of Planetary Systems from Thales to Kepler." Revised foreword by W. H. Stahl. xvii + 430pp. 5⅜ x 8.
S79 Paperbound **$1.98**

A CONCISE HISTORY OF MATHEMATICS, D. Struik. Lucid study of development of ideas, techniques, from Ancient Near East, Greece, Islamic science, Middle Ages, Renaissance, modern times. Important mathematicians described in detail. Treatment not anecdotal, but analytical development of ideas. Non-technical—no math training needed. "Rich in content, thoughtful in interpretations," U.S. Quarterly Booklist. 60 illustrations including Greek, Egyptian manuscripts, portraits of 31 mathematicians. 2nd edition. xix + 299pp. 5⅜ x 8.
S255 Paperbound **$1.75**

THE PHILOSOPHICAL WRITINGS OF PEIRCE, edited by Justus Buchler. A carefully balanced expositon of Peirce's complete system, written by Peirce himself. It covers such matters as scientific method, pure chance vs. law, symbolic logic, theory of signs, pragmatism, experiment, and other topics. "Excellent selection . . . gives more than adequate evidence of the range and greatness," Personalist. Formerly entitled "The Philosophy of Peirce." xvi + 368pp.
T217 Paperbound **$1.95**

SCIENCE AND METHOD, Henri Poincaré. Procedure of scientific discovery, methodology, experiment, idea-germination—processes by which discoveries come into being. Most significant and interesting aspects of development, application of ideas. Chapters cover selection of facts, chance, mathematical reasoning, mathematics and logic; Whitehead, Russell, Cantor, the new mechanics, etc. 288pp. 5⅜ x 8.
S222 Paperbound **$1.35**

SCIENCE AND HYPOTHESIS, Henri Poincaré. Creative psychology in science. How such concepts as number, magnitude, space, force, classical mechanics developed, how modern scientist uses them in his thought. Hypothesis in physics, theories of modern physics. Introduction by Sir James Larmor. "Few mathematicians have had the breadth of vision of Poincaré, and none is his superior in the gift of clear exposition," E. T. Bell. 272pp. 5⅜ x 8.
S221 Paperbound **$1.35**

ESSAYS IN EXPERIMENTAL LOGIC, John Dewey. Stimulating series of essays by one of most influential minds in American philosophy presents some of his most mature thoughts on wide range of subjects. Partial contents: Relationship between inquiry and experience; dependence of knowledge upon thought; character logic; judgments of practice, data, and meanings; stimuli of thought, etc. viii + 444pp. 5⅜ x 8.
T73 Paperbound **$1.95**

WHAT IS SCIENCE, Norman Campbell. Excellent introduction explains scientific method, role of mathematics, types of scientific laws. Contents: 2 aspects of science, science and nature, laws of chance, discovery of laws, explanation of laws, measurement and numerical laws, applications of science. 192pp. 5⅜ x 8.
S43 Paperbound **$1.25**

FROM EUCLID TO EDDINGTON: A STUDY OF THE CONCEPTIONS OF THE EXTERNAL WORLD, Sir Edmund Whittaker. Foremost British scientist traces development of theories of natural philosophy from western rediscovery of Euclid to Eddington, Einstein, Dirac, etc. 5 major divisions: Space, Time and Movement; Concepts of Classical Physics; Concepts of Quantum Mechanics; Eddington Universe. Contrasts inadequacy of classical physics to understand physical world with present day attempts of relativity, non-Euclidean geometry, space curvature, etc. 212pp. 5⅜ x 8. T491 Paperbound **$1.35**

THE ANALYSIS OF MATTER, Bertrand Russell. How do our senses accord with the new physics? This volume covers such topics as logical analysis of physics, prerelativity physics, causality, scientific inference, physics and perception, special and general relativity, Weyl's theory, tensors, invariants and their physical interpretation, periodicity and qualitative series. "The most thorough treatment of the subject that has yet been published," The Nation. Introduction by L. E. Denonn. 422pp. 5⅜ x 8. T231 Paperbound **$1.95**

LANGUAGE, TRUTH, AND LOGIC, A. Ayer. A clear introduction to the Vienna and Cambridge schools of Logical Positivism. Specific tests to evaluate validity of ideas, etc. Contents: function of philosophy, elimination of metaphysics, nature of analysis, a priori, truth and probability, etc. 10th printing. "I should like to have written it myself," Bertrand Russell. 160pp. 5⅜ x 8. T10 Paperbound **$1.25**

THE PSYCHOLOGY OF INVENTION IN THE MATHEMATICAL FIELD, J. Hadamard. Where do ideas come from? What role does the unconscious play? Are ideas best developed by mathematical reasoning, word reasoning, visualization? What are the methods used by Einstein, Poincaré, Galton, Riemann? How can these techniques be applied by others? One of the world's leading mathematicians discusses these and other questions. xiii + 145pp. 5⅜ x 8. T107 Paperbound **$1.25**

GUIDE TO PHILOSOPHY, C. E. M. Joad. By one of the ablest expositors of all time, this is not simply a history or a typological survey, but an examination of central problems in terms of answers afforded by the greatest thinkers: Plato, Aristotle, Scholastics, Leibniz, Kant, Whitehead, Russell, and many others. Especially valuable to persons in the physical sciences; over 100 pages devoted to Jeans, Eddington, and others, the philosophy of modern physics, scientific materialism, pragmatism, etc. Classified bibliography. 592pp. 5⅜ x 8. T50 Paperbound **$2.00**

SUBSTANCE AND FUNCTION, and EINSTEIN'S THEORY OF RELATIVITY, Ernst Cassirer. Two books bound as one. Cassirer establishes a philosophy of the exact sciences that takes into consideration new developments in mathematics, shows historical connections. Partial contents: Aristotelian logic, Mill's analysis, Helmholtz and Kronecker, Russell and cardinal numbers, Euclidean vs. non-Euclidean geometry, Einstein's relativity. Bibliography. Index. xxi + 464pp. 5⅜ x 8. T50 Paperbound **$2.00**

FOUNDATIONS OF GEOMETRY, Bertrand Russell. Nobel laureate analyzes basic problems in the overlap area between mathematics and philosophy: the nature of geometrical knowledge, the nature of geometry, and the applications of geometry to space. Covers history of non-Euclidean geometry, philosophic interpretations of geometry, especially Kant, projective and metrical geometry. Most interesting as the solution offered in 1897 by a great mind to a problem still current. New introduction by Prof. Morris Kline, N.Y. University. "Admirably clear, precise, and elegantly reasoned analysis," International Math. News. xii + 201pp. 5⅜ x 8. S233 Paperbound **$1.60**

THE NATURE OF PHYSICAL THEORY, P. W. Bridgman. How modern physics looks to a highly unorthodox physicist—a Nobel laureate. Pointing out many absurdities of science, demonstrating inadequacies of various physical theories, weighs and analyzes contributions of Einstein, Bohr, Heisenberg, many others. A non-technical consideration of correlation of science and reality. xi + 138pp. 5⅜ x 8. S33 Paperbound **$1.25**

EXPERIMENT AND THEORY IN PHYSICS, Max Born. A Nobel laureate examines the nature and value of the counterclaims of experiment and theory in physics. Synthetic versus analytical scientific advances are analyzed in works of Einstein, Bohr, Heisenberg, Planck, Eddington, Milne, others, by a fellow scientist. 44pp. 5⅜ x 8. S308 Paperbound **60¢**

A SHORT HISTORY OF ANATOMY AND PHYSIOLOGY FROM THE GREEKS TO HARVEY, Charles Singer. Corrected edition of "The Evolution of Anatomy." Classic traces anatomy, physiology from prescientific times through Greek, Roman periods, dark ages, Renaissance, to beginning of modern concepts. Centers on individuals, movements, that definitely advanced anatomical knowledge. Plato, Diocles, Erasistratus, Galen, da Vinci, etc. Special section on Vesalius. 20 plates. 270 extremely interesting illustrations of ancient, Medieval, Renaissance, Oriental origin. xii + 209pp. 5⅜ x 8. T389 Paperbound **$1.75**

SPACE-TIME-MATTER, Hermann Weyl. "The standard treatise on the general theory of relativity," (Nature), by world renowned scientist. Deep, clear discussion of logical coherence of general theory, introducing all needed tools: Maxwell, analytical geometry, non-Euclidean geometry, tensor calculus, etc. Basis is classical space-time, before absorption of relativity. Contents: Euclidean space, mathematical form, metrical continuum, general theory, etc. 15 diagrams. xviii + 330pp. 5⅜ x 8. S267 Paperbound **$1.75**

MATTER AND MOTION, James Clerk Maxwell. Excellent exposition begins with simple particles, proceeds gradually to physical systems beyond complete analysis; motion, force, properties of centre of mass of material system; work, energy, gravitation, etc. Written with all Maxwell's original insights and clarity. Notes by E. Larmor. 17 diagrams. 178pp. 5⅜ x 8.
S188 Paperbound **$1.25**

PRINCIPLES OF MECHANICS, Heinrich Hertz. Last work by the great 19th century physicist is not only a classic, but of great interest in the logic of science. Creating a new system of mechanics based upon space, time, and mass, it returns to axiomatic analysis, understanding of the formal or structural aspects of science, taking into account logic, observation, a priori elements. Of great historical importance to Poincaré, Carnap, Einstein, Milne. A 20 page introduction by R. S. Cohen, Wesleyan University, analyzes the implications of Hertz's thought and the logic of science. 13 page introduction by Helmholtz. xlii + 274pp. 5⅜ x 8.
S316 Clothbound **$3.50**
S317 Paperbound **$1.75**

FROM MAGIC TO SCIENCE, Charles Singer. A great historian examines aspects of science from Roman Empire through Renaissance. Includes perhaps best discussion of early herbals, penetrating physiological interpretation of "The Visions of Hildegarde of Bingen." Also examines Arabian, Galenic influences; Pythagoras' sphere, Paracelsus; reawakening of science under Leonardo da Vinci, Vesalius; Lorica of Gildas the Briton; etc. Frequent quotations with translations from contemporary manuscripts. Unabridged, corrected edition. 158 unusual illustrations from Classical, Medieval sources. xxvii + 365pp. 5⅜ x 8.
T390 Paperbound **$2.00**

A HISTORY OF THE CALCULUS, AND ITS CONCEPTUAL DEVELOPMENT, Carl B. Boyer. Provides laymen, mathematicians a detailed history of the development of the calculus, from beginnings in antiquity to final elaboration as mathematical abstraction. Gives a sense of mathematics not as technique, but as habit of mind, in progression of ideas of Zeno, Plato, Pythagoras, Eudoxus, Arabic and Scholastic mathematicians, Newton, Leibniz, Taylor, Descartes, Euler, Lagrange, Cantor, Weierstrass, and others. This first comprehensive, critical history of the calculus was originally entitled "The Concepts of the Calculus." Foreword by R. Courant. 22 figures. 25 page bibliography. v + 364pp. 5⅜ x 8.
S509 Paperbound **$2.00**

A DIDEROT PICTORIAL ENCYCLOPEDIA OF TRADES AND INDUSTRY, Manufacturing and the Technical Arts in Plates Selected from "L'Encyclopédie ou Dictionnaire Raisonné des Sciences, des Arts, et des Métiers" of Denis Diderot. Edited with text by C. Gillispie. First modern selection of plates from high-point of 18th century French engraving. Storehouse of technological information to historian of arts and science. Over 2,000 illustrations on 485 full page plates, most of them original size, show trades, industries of fascinating era in such great detail that modern reconstructions might be made of them. Plates teem with men, women, children performing thousands of operations; show sequence, general operations, closeups, details of machinery. Illustrates such important, interesting trades, industries as sowing, harvesting, beekeeping, tobacco processing, fishing, arts of war, mining, smelting, casting iron, extracting mercury, making gunpowder, cannons, bells, shoeing horses, tanning, papermaking, printing, dying, over 45 more categories. Professor Gillispie of Princeton supplies full commentary on all plates, identifies operations, tools, processes, etc. Material is presented in lively, lucid fashion. Of great interest to all studying history of science, technology. Heavy library cloth. 920pp. 9 x 12.
T421 2 volume set **$18.50**

DE MAGNETE, William Gilbert. Classic work on magnetism, founded new science. Gilbert was first to use word "electricity," to recognize mass as distinct from weight, to discover effect of heat on magnetic bodies; invented an electroscope, differentiated between static electricity and magnetism, conceived of earth as magnet. This lively work, by first great experimental scientist, is not only a valuable historical landmark, but a delightfully easy to follow record of a searching, ingenious mind. Translated by P. F. Mottelay. 25 page biographical memoir. 90 figures. lix + 368pp. 5⅜ x 8.
S470 Paperbound **$2.00**

HISTORY OF MATHEMATICS, D. E. Smith. Most comprehensive, non-technical history of math in English. Discusses lives and works of over a thousand major, minor figures, with footnotes giving technical information outside book's scheme, and indicating disputed matters. Vol. I: A chronological examination, from primitive concepts through Egypt, Babylonia, Greece, the Orient, Rome, the Middle Ages, The Renaissance, and to 1900. Vol. II: The development of ideas in specific fields and problems, up through elementary calculus. "Marks an epoch . . . will modify the entire teaching of the history of science," George Sarton. 2 volumes, total of 510 illustrations, 1355pp. 5⅜ x 8. Set boxed in attractive container.
T429, 430 Paperbound, the set **$5.00**

THE PHILOSOPHY OF SPACE AND TIME, H. Reichenbach. An important landmark in development of empiricist conception of geometry, covering foundations of geometry, time theory, consequences of Einstein's relativity, including: relations between theory and observations; coordinate definitions; relations between topological and metrical properties of space; psychological problem of visual intuition of non-Euclidean structures; many more topics important to modern science and philosophy. Majority of ideas require only knowledge of intermediate math. "Still the best book in the field," Rudolf Carnap. Introduction by R. Carnap. 49 figures. xviii + 296pp. 5⅜ x 8.
S443 Paperbound **$2.00**

FOUNDATIONS OF SCIENCE: THE PHILOSOPHY OF THEORY AND EXPERIMENT, N. Campbell. A critique of the most fundamental concepts of science, particularly physics. Examines why certain propositions are accepted without question, demarcates science from philosophy, etc. Part I analyzes presuppositions of scientific thought: existence of material world, nature of laws, probability, etc; part 2 covers nature of experiment and applications of mathematics: conditions for measurement, relations between numerical laws and theories, error, etc. An appendix covers problems arising from relativity, force, motion, space, time. A classic in its field. "A real grasp of what science is," Higher Educational Journal. xiii + 565pp. 5⅝ x 8⅜. S372 Paperbound **$2.95**

THE STUDY OF THE HISTORY OF MATHEMATICS and **THE STUDY OF THE HISTORY OF SCIENCE, G. Sarton.** Excellent introductions, orientation, for beginning or mature worker. Describes duty of mathematical historian, incessant efforts and genius of previous generations. Explains how today's discipline differs from previous methods. 200 item bibliography with critical evaluations, best available biographies of modern mathematicians, best treatises on historical methods is especially valuable. 10 illustrations. 2 volumes bound as one. 113pp. + 75pp. 5⅜ x 8. T240 Paperbound **$1.25**

MATHEMATICAL PUZZLES

MATHEMATICAL PUZZLES OF SAM LOYD, selected and edited by **Martin Gardner.** 117 choice puzzles by greatest American puzzle creator and innovator, from his famous "Cyclopedia of Puzzles." All unique style, historical flavor of originals. Based on arithmetic, algebra, probability, game theory, route tracing, topology, sliding block, operations research, geometrical dissection. Includes famous "14-15" puzzle which was national craze, "Horse of a Different Color" which sold millions of copies. 120 line drawings, diagrams. Solutions. xx + 167pp. 5⅜ x 8. T498 Paperbound **$1.00**

SYMBOLIC LOGIC and THE GAME OF LOGIC, Lewis Carroll. "Symbolic Logic" is not concerned with modern symbolic logic, but is instead a collection of over 380 problems posed with charm and imagination, using the syllogism, and a fascinating diagrammatic method of drawing conclusions. In "The Game of Logic" Carroll's whimsical imagination devises a logical game played with 2 diagrams and counters (included) to manipulate hundreds of tricky syllogisms. The final section, "Hit or Miss" is a lagniappe of 101 additional puzzles in the delightful Carroll manner. Until this reprint edition, both of these books were rarities costing up to $15 each. Symbolic Logic: Index. xxxi + 199pp. The Game of Logic: 96pp. 2 vols. bound as one. 5⅜ x 8. T492 Paperbound **$1.50**

PILLOW PROBLEMS and A TANGLED TALE, Lewis Carroll. One of the rarest of all Carroll's works, "Pillow Problems" contains 72 original math puzzles, all typically ingenious. Particularly fascinating are Carroll's answers which remain exactly as he thought them out, reflecting his actual mental process. The problems in "A Tangled Tale" are in story form, originally appearing as a monthly magazine serial. Carroll not only gives the solutions, but uses answers sent in by readers to discuss wrong approaches and misleading paths, and grades them for insight. Both of these books were rarities until this edition, "Pillow Problems" costing up to $25, and "A Tangled Tale" $15. Pillow Problems: Preface and Introduction by Lewis Carroll. xx + 109pp. A Tangled Tale: 6 illustrations. 152pp. Two vols. bound as one. 5⅜ x 8. T493 Paperbound **$1.50**

NEW WORD PUZZLES, G. L. Kaufman. 100 brand new challenging puzzles on words, combinations, never before published. Most are new types invented by author, for beginners and experts both. Squares of letters follow chess moves to build words; symmetrical designs made of synonyms; rhymed crostics; double word squares; syllable puzzles where you fill in missing syllables instead of missing letter; many other types, all new. Solutions. "Excellent," Recreation. 100 puzzles. 196 figures. vi + 122pp. 5⅜ x 8. T344 Paperbound **$1.00**

MATHEMATICAL EXCURSIONS, H. A. Merrill. Fun, recreation, insights into elementary problem solving. Math expert guides you on by-paths not generally travelled in elementary math courses—divide by inspection, Russian peasant multiplication; memory systems for pi; odd, even magic squares; dyadic systems; square roots by geometry; Tchebichev's machine; dozens more. Solutions to more difficult ones. "Brain stirring stuff . . . a classic," Genie. 50 illustrations. 145pp. 5⅜ x 8. T350 Paperbound **$1.00**

THE BOOK OF MODERN PUZZLES, G. L. Kaufman. Over 150 puzzles, absolutely all new material based on same appeal as crosswords, deduction puzzles, but with different principles, techniques. 2-minute teasers, word labyrinths, design, pattern, logic, observation puzzles, puzzles testing ability to apply general knowledge to peculiar situations, many others. Solutions. 116 illustrations. 192pp. 5⅜ x 8. T143 Paperbound **$1.00**

MATHEMAGIC, MAGIC PUZZLES, AND GAMES WITH NUMBERS, R. V. Heath. Over 60 puzzles, stunts, on properties of numbers. Easy techniques for multiplying large numbers mentally, identifying unknown numbers, finding date of any day in any year. Includes The Lost Digit, 3 Acrobats, Psychic Bridge, magic squares, triangles, cubes, others not easily found elsewhere. Edited by J. S. Meyer. 76 illustrations. 128pp. 5⅜ x 8. T110 Paperbound **$1.00**

PUZZLE QUIZ AND STUNT FUN, J. Meyer. 238 high-priority puzzles, stunts, tricks—math puzzles like The Clever Carpenter, Atom Bomb, Please Help Alice; mysteries, deductions like The Bridge of Sighs, Secret Code; observation puzzlers like The American Flag, Playing Cards, Telephone Dial; over 200 others with magic squares, tongue twisters, puns, anagrams. Solutions. Revised, enlarged edition of "Fun-To-Do." Over 100 illustrations. 238 puzzles, stunts, tricks. 256pp. 5⅜ x 8.
T337 Paperbound **$1.00**

101 PUZZLES IN THOUGHT AND LOGIC, C. R. Wylie, Jr. For readers who enjoy challenge, stimulation of logical puzzles without specialized math or scientific knowledge. Problems entirely new, range from relatively easy to brainteasers for hours of subtle entertainment. Detective puzzles, find the lying fisherman, how a blind man identifies color by logic, many more. Easy-to-understand introduction to logic of puzzle solving and general scientific method. 128pp. 5⅜ x 8.
T367 Paperbound **$1.00**

CRYPTANALYSIS, H. F. Gaines. Standard elementary, intermediate text for serious students. Not just old material, but much not generally known, except to experts. Concealment, Transposition, Substitution ciphers; Vigenere, Kasiski, Playfair, multafid, dozens of other techniques. Formerly "Elementary Cryptanalysis." Appendix with sequence charts, letter frequencies in English, 5 other languages, English word frequencies. Bibliography. 167 codes. New to this edition: solutions to codes. vi + 230pp. 5⅜ x 8⅜.
T97 Paperbound **$1.95**

CRYPTOGRAPHY, L. D. Smith. Excellent elementary introduction to enciphering, deciphering secret writing. Explains transposition, substitution ciphers; codes; solutions; geometrical patterns, route transcription, columnar transposition, other methods. Mixed cipher systems; single, polyalphabetical substitutions; mechanical devices; Vigenere; etc. Enciphering Japanese; explanation of Baconian biliteral cipher; frequency tables. Over 150 problems. Bibliography. Index. 164pp. 5⅜ x 8.
T247 Paperbound **$1.00**

MATHEMATICS, MAGIC AND MYSTERY, M. Gardner. Card tricks, metal mathematics, stage mind-reading, other "magic" explained as applications of probability, sets, number theory, etc. Creative examination of laws, applications. Scores of new tricks, insights. 115 sections on cards, dice, coins; vanishing tricks, many others. No sleight of hand—math guarantees success. "Could hardly get more entertainment . . . easy to follow," Mathematics Teacher. 115 illustrations. xii + 174pp. 5⅜ x 8.
T335 Paperbound **$1.00**

AMUSEMENTS IN MATHEMATICS, H. E. Dudeney. Foremost British originator of math puzzles, always witty, intriguing, paradoxical in this classic. One of largest collections. More than 430 puzzles, problems, paradoxes. Mazes, games, problems on number manipulations, unicursal, other route problems, puzzles on measuring, weighing, packing, age, kinship, chessboards, joiners', crossing river, plane figure dissection, many others. Solutions. More than 450 illustrations. viii + 258pp. 5⅜ x 8.
T473 Paperbound **$1.25**

THE CANTERBURY PUZZLES H. E. Dudeney. Chaucer's pilgrims set one another problems in story form. Also Adventures of the Puzzle Club, the Strange Escape of the King's Jester, the Monks of Riddlewell, the Squire's Christmas Puzzle Party, others. All puzzles are original, based on dissecting plane figures, arithmetic, algebra, elementary calculus, other branches of mathematics, and purely logical ingenuity. "The limit of ingenuity and intricacy," The Observer. Over 110 puzzles, full solutions. 150 illustrations. viii + 225 pp. 5⅜ x 8.
T474 Paperbound **$1.25**

MATHEMATICAL PUZZLES FOR BEGINNERS AND ENTHUSIASTS, G. Mott-Smith. 188 puzzles to test mental agility. Inference, interpretation, algebra, dissection of plane figures, geometry, properties of numbers, decimation, permutations, probability, all are in these delightful problems. Includes the Odic Force, How to Draw an Ellipse, Spider's Cousin, more than 180 others. Detailed solutions. Appendix with square roots, triangular numbers, primes, etc. 135 illustrations. 2nd revised edition. 248pp. 5⅜ x 8.
T198 Paperbound **$1.00**

MATHEMATICAL RECREATIONS, M. Kraitchik. Some 250 puzzles, problems, demonstrations of recreation mathematics on relatively advanced level. Unusual historical problems from Greek, Medieval, Arabic, Hindu sources; modern problems on "mathematics without numbers," geometry, topology, arithmetic, etc. Pastimes derived from figurative, Mersenne, Fermat numbers; fairy chess; latruncles: reversi; etc. Full solutions. Excellent insights into special fields of math. "Strongly recommended to all who are interested in the lighter side of mathematics," Mathematical Gaz. 181 illustrations. 330pp. 5⅜ x 8.
T163 Paperbound **$1.75**

FICTION

FLATLAND, E. A. Abbott. A perennially popular science-fiction classic about life in a 2-dimensional world, and the impingement of higher dimensions. Political, satiric, humorous, moral overtones. This land where women are straight lines and the lowest and most dangerous classes are isosceles triangles with 3° vertices conveys brilliantly a feeling for many concepts of modern science. 7th edition. New introduction by Banesh Hoffmann. 128pp. 5⅜ x 8.
T1 Paperbound **$1.00**

SEVEN SCIENCE FICTION NOVELS OF H. G. WELLS. Complete texts, unabridged, of seven of Wells' greatest novels: The War of the Worlds, The Invisible Man, The Island of Dr. Moreau, The Food of the Gods, First Men in the Moon, In the Days of the Comet, The Time Machine. Still considered by many experts to be the best science-fiction ever written, they will offer amusements and instruction to the scientific minded reader. "The great master," Sky and Telescope. 1051pp. 5⅜ x 8.   **T264 Clothbound $3.95**

28 SCIENCE FICTION STORIES OF H. G. WELLS. Unabridged! This enormous omnibus contains 2 full length novels—Men Like Gods, Star Begotten—plus 26 short stories of space, time, invention, biology, etc. The Crystal Egg, The Country of the Blind, Empire of the Ants, The Man Who Could Work Miracles, Aepyornis Island, A Story of the Days to Come, and 20 others "A master . . . not surpassed by . . . writers of today," The English Journal. 915pp. 5⅜ x 8.   **T265 Clothbound $3.95**

FIVE ADVENTURE NOVELS OF H. RIDER HAGGARD. All the mystery and adventure of darkest Africa captured accurately by a man who lived among Zulus for years, who knew African ethnology, folkways as did few of his contemporaries. They have been regarded as examples of the very best high adventure by such critics as Orwell, Andrew Lang, Kipling. Contents: She, King Solomon's Mines, Allan Quatermain, Allan's Wife, Maiwa's Revenge. "Could spin a yarn so full of suspense and color that you couldn't put the story down," Sat. Review. 821pp. 5⅜ x 8.   **T108 Clothbound $3.95**

CHESS AND CHECKERS

LEARN CHESS FROM THE MASTERS, Fred Reinfeld. Easiest, most instructive way to improve your game—play 10 games against such masters as Marshall, Znosko-Borovsky, Bronstein, Najdorf, etc., with each move graded by easy system. Includes ratings for alternate moves possible. Games selected for interest, clarity, easily isolated principles. Covers Ruy Lopez, Dutch Defense, Vienna Game openings; subtle, intricate middle game variations; all-important end game. Full annotations. Formerly "Chess by Yourself." 91 diagrams. viii + 144pp. 5⅜ x 8.   **T362 Paperbound $1.00**

REINFELD ON THE END GAME IN CHESS, Fred Reinfeld. Analyzes 62 end games by Alekhine, Flohr, Tarrasch, Morphy, Capablanca, Rubinstein, Lasker, Reshevsky, other masters. Only 1st rate book with extensive coverage of error—tell exactly what is wrong with each move you might have made. Centers around transitions from middle play to end play. King and pawn, minor pieces, queen endings; blockage, weak, passed pawns, etc. "Excellent . . . a boon," Chess Life. Formerly "Practical End Play." 62 figures. vi + 177pp. 5⅜ x 8.   **T417 Paperbound $1.25**

HYPERMODERN CHESS as developed in the games of its greatest exponent, ARON NIMZOVICH, edited by Fred Reinfeld. An intensely original player, analyst, Nimzovich's approaches startled, often angered the chess world. This volume, designed for the average player, shows how his iconoclastic methods won him victories over Alekhine, Lasker, Marshall, Rubinstein, Spielmann, others, and infused new life into the game. Use his methods to startle opponents, invigorate play. "Annotations and introductions to each game . . . are excellent," Times (London). 180 diagrams. viii + 220pp. 5⅜ x 8.   **T448 Paperbound $1.35**

THE ADVENTURE OF CHESS, Edward Lasker. Lively reader, by one of America's finest chess masters, including: history of chess, from ancient Indian 4-handed game of Chaturanga to great players of today; such delights and oddities as Maelzel's chess-playing automaton that beat Napoleon 3 times; etc. One of most valuable features is author's personal recollections of men he has played against—Nimzovich, Emanuel Lasker, Capablanca, Alekhine, etc. Discussion of chess-playing machines (newly revised). 5 page chess primer. 11 illustrations. 53 diagrams. 296pp. 5⅜ x 8.   **S510 Paperbound $1.45**

THE ART OF CHESS, James Mason. Unabridged reprinting of latest revised edition of most famous general study ever written. Mason, early 20th century master, teaches beginning, intermediate player over 90 openings; middle game, end game, to see more moves ahead, to plan purposefully, attack, sacrifice, defend, exchange, govern general strategy. "Classic . . . one of the clearest and best developed studies," Publishers Weekly. Also included, a complete supplement by F. Reinfeld, "How Do You Play Chess?", invaluable to beginners for its lively question-and-answer method. 448 diagrams. 1947 Reinfeld-Bernstein text. Bibliography. xvi + 340pp. 5⅜ x 8.   **T463 Paperbound $1.85**

MORPHY'S GAMES OF CHESS, edited by P. W. Sergeant. Put boldness into your game by flowing brilliant, forceful moves of the greatest chess player of all time. 300 of Morphy's best games, carefully annotated to reveal principles. 54 classics against masters like Anderssen, Harrwitz, Bird, Paulsen, and others. 52 games at odds; 54 blindfold games; plus over 100 others. Follow his interpretation of Dutch Defense, Evans Gambit, Giuoco Piano, Ruy Lopez, many more. Unabridged reissue of latest revised edition. New introduction by F. Reinfeld. Annotations, introduction by Sergeant. 235 diagrams. x + 352pp. 5⅜ x 8.   **T386 Paperbound $1.75**

DOVER SCIENCE BOOKS

WIN AT CHECKERS, M. Hopper. (Formerly "Checkers.") Former World's Unrestricted Checker Champion discusses principles of game, expert's shots, traps, problems for beginner, standard openings, locating best move, end game, opening "blitzkrieg" moves to draw when behind, etc. Over 100 detailed questions, answers anticipate problems. Appendix. 75 problems with solutions, diagrams. 79 figures. xi + 107pp. 5⅜ x 8.   T363 Paperbound **$1.00**

HOW TO FORCE CHECKMATE, Fred Reinfeld. If you have trouble finishing off your opponent, here is a collection of lightning strokes and combinations from actual tournament play. Starts with 1-move checkmates, works up to 3-move mates. Develops ability to look ahead, gain new insights into combinations, complex or deceptive positions; ways to estimate weaknesses, strengths of you and your opponent. "A good deal of amusement and instruction," Times, (London). 300 diagrams. Solutions to all positions. Formerly "Challenge to Chess Players." 111pp. 5⅜ x 8.   T417 Paperbound **$1.25**

A TREASURY OF CHESS LORE, edited by Fred Reinfeld. Delightful collection of anecdotes, short stories, aphorisms by, about masters; poems, accounts of games, tournaments, photographs; hundreds of humorous, pithy, satirical, wise, historical episodes, comments, word portraits. Fascinating "must" for chess players; revealing and perhaps seductive to those who wonder what their friends see in game. 49 photographs (14 full page plates). 12 diagrams. xi + 306pp. 5⅜ x 8.   T458 Paperbound **$1.75**

WIN AT CHESS, Fred Reinfeld. 300 practical chess situations, to sharpen your eye, test skill against masters. Start with simple examples, progress at own pace to complexities. This selected series of crucial moments in chess will stimulate imagination, develop stronger, more versatile game. Simple grading system enables you to judge progress. "Extensive use of diagrams is a great attraction," Chess. 300 diagrams. Notes, solutions to every situation. Formerly "Chess Quiz." vi + 120pp. 5⅜ x 8.   T433 Paperbound **$1.00**

MATHEMATICS:
ELEMENTARY TO INTERMEDIATE

HOW TO CALCULATE QUICKLY, H. Sticker. Tried and true method to help mathematics of everyday life. Awakens "number sense"—ability to see relationships between numbers as whole quantities. A serious course of over 9000 problems and their solutions through techniques not taught in schools: left-to-right multiplications, new fast division, etc. 10 minutes a day will double or triple calculation speed. Excellent for scientist at home in higher math, but dissatisfied with speed and accuracy in lower math. 256pp. 5 x 7¼.
Paperbound **$1.00**

FAMOUS PROBLEMS OF ELEMENTARY GEOMETRY, Felix Klein. Expanded version of 1894 Easter lectures at Göttingen. 3 problems of classical geometry: squaring the circle, trisecting angle, doubling cube, considered with full modern implications: transcendental numbers, pi, etc. "A modern classic . . . no knowledge of higher mathematics is required," Scientia. Notes by R. Archibald. 16 figures. xi + 92pp. 5⅜ x 8.   T298 Paperbound **$1.00**

HIGHER MATHEMATICS FOR STUDENTS OF CHEMISTRY AND PHYSICS, J. W. Mellor. Practical, not abstract, building problems out of familiar laboratory material. Covers differential calculus, coordinate, analytical geometry, functions, integral calculus, infinite series, numerical equations, differential equations, Fourier's theorem probability, theory of errors, calculus of variations, determinants. "If the reader is not familiar with this book, it will repay him to examine it," Chem. and Engineering News. 800 problems. 189 figures. xxi + 641pp. 5⅜ x 8.   S193 Paperbound **$2.25**

TRIGONOMETRY REFRESHER FOR TECHNICAL MEN, A. A. Klaf. 913 detailed questions, answers cover most important aspects of plane, spherical trigonometry—particularly useful in clearing up difficulties in special areas. Part I: plane trig, angles, quadrants, functions, graphical representation, interpolation, equations, logs, solution of triangle, use of slide rule, etc. Next 188 pages discuss applications to navigation, surveying, elasticity, architecture, other special fields. Part 3: spherical trig, applications to terrestrial, astronomical problems. Methods of time-saving, simplification of principal angles, make book most useful. 913 questions answered. 1738 problems, answers to odd numbers. 494 figures. 24 pages of formulas, functions. x + 629pp. 5⅜ x 8.   T371 Paperbound **$2.00**

CALCULUS REFRESHER FOR TECHNICAL MEN, A. A. Klaf. 756 questions examine most important aspects of integral, differential calculus. Part I: simple differential calculus, constants, variables, functions, increments, logs, curves, etc. Part 2: fundamental ideas of integrations, inspection, substitution, areas, volumes, mean value, double, triple integration, etc. Practical aspects stressed. 50 pages illustrate applications to specific problems of civil, nautical engineering, electricity, stress, strain, elasticity, similar fields. 756 questions answered. 566 problems, mostly answered. 36pp. of useful constants, formulas. v + 431pp. 5⅜ x 8.   T370 Paperbound **$2.00**

MONOGRAPHS ON TOPICS OF MODERN MATHEMATICS, edited by J. W. A. Young. Advanced mathematics for persons who have forgotten, or not gone beyond, high school algebra. 9 monographs on foundation of geometry, modern pure geometry, non-Euclidean geometry, fundamental propositions of algebra, algebraic equations, functions, calculus, theory of numbers, etc. Each monograph gives proofs of important results, and descriptions of leading methods, to provide wide coverage. "Of high merit," Scientific American. New introduction by Prof. M. Kline, N.Y. Univ. 100 diagrams. xvi + 416pp. 6⅛ x 9¼.
S289 Paperbound **$2.00**

MATHEMATICS IN ACTION, O. G. Sutton. Excellent middle level application of mathematics to study of universe, demonstrates how math is applied to ballistics, theory of computing machines, waves, wave-like phenomena, theory of fluid flow, meteorological problems, statistics, flight, similar phenomena. No knowledge of advanced math required. Differential equations, Fourier series, group concepts, Eigenfunctions, Planck's constant, airfoil theory, and similar topics explained so clearly in everyday language that almost anyone can derive benefit from reading this even if much of high-school math is forgotten. 2nd edition. 88 figures. viii + 236pp. 5⅜ x 8.
T450 Clothbound **$3.50**

ELEMENTARY MATHEMATICS FROM AN ADVANCED STANDPOINT, Felix Klein. Classic text, an outgrowth of Klein's famous integration and survey course at Göttingen. Using one field to interpret, adjust another, it covers basic topics in each area, with extensive analysis. Especially valuable in areas of modern mathematics. "A great mathematician, inspiring teacher, . . . deep insight," Bul., Amer. Math Soc.

Vol. I. ARITHMETIC, ALGEBRA, ANALYSIS. Introduces concept of function immediately, enlivens discussion with graphical, geometric methods. Partial contents: natural numbers, special properties, complex numbers. Real equations with real unknowns, complex quantities. Logarithmic, exponential functions, infinitesimal calculus. Transcendence of e and pi, theory of assemblages. Index. 125 figures. ix + 274pp. 5⅜ x 8.
S151 Paperbound **$1.75**

Vol. II. GEOMETRY. Comprehensive view, accompanies space perception inherent in geometry with analytic formulas which facilitate precise formulation. Partial contents: Simplest geometric manifold; line segments, Grassman determinant principles, classification of configurations of space. Geometric transformations: affine, projective, higher point transformations, theory of the imaginary. Systematic discussion of geometry and its foundations. 141 illustrations. ix + 214pp. 5⅜ x 8.
S151 Paperbound **$1.75**

A TREATISE ON PLANE AND ADVANCED TRIGONOMETRY, E. W. Hobson. Extraordinarily wide coverage, going beyond usual college level, one of few works covering advanced trig in full detail. By a great expositor with unerring anticipation of potentially difficult points. Includes circular functions; expansion of functions of multiple angle; trig tables; relations between sides, angles of triangles; complex numbers; etc. Many problems fully solved. "The best work on the subject," Nature. Formerly entitled "A Treatise on Plane Trigonometry." 689 examples. 66 figures. xvi + 383pp. 5⅜ x 8.
S353 Paperbound **$1.95**

NON-EUCLIDEAN GEOMETRY, Roberto Bonola. The standard coverage of non-Euclidean geometry. Examines from both a historical and mathematical point of view geometries which have arisen from a study of Euclid's 5th postulate on parallel lines. Also included are complete texts, translated, of Bolyai's "Theory of Absolute Space," Lobachevsky's "Theory of Parallels." 180 diagrams. 431pp. 5⅜ x 8.
S27 Paperbound **$1.95**

GEOMETRY OF FOUR DIMENSIONS, H. P. Manning. Unique in English as a clear, concise introduction. Treatment is synthetic, mostly Euclidean, though in hyperplanes and hyperspheres at infinity, non-Euclidean geometry is used. Historical introduction. Foundations of 4-dimensional geometry. Perpendicularity, simple angles. Angles of planes, higher order. Symmetry, order, motion; hyperpyramids, hypercones, hyperspheres; figures with parallel elements; volume, hypervolume in space; regular polyhedroids. Glossary. 78 figures. ix + 348pp. 5⅜ x 8.
S182 Paperbound **$1.95**

MATHEMATICS: INTERMEDIATE TO ADVANCED

GEOMETRY (EUCLIDEAN AND NON-EUCLIDEAN)

THE GEOMETRY OF RENÉ DESCARTES. With this book, Descartes founded analytical geometry. Original French text, with Descartes's own diagrams, and excellent Smith-Latham translation. Contains: Problems the Construction of Which Requires only Straight Lines and Circles; On the Nature of Curved Lines; On the Construction of Solid or Supersolid Problems. Diagrams. 258pp. 5⅜ x 8.
S68 Paperbound **$1.50**

DOVER SCIENCE BOOKS

THE WORKS OF ARCHIMEDES, edited by T. L. Heath. All the known works of the great Greek mathematician, including the recently discovered Method of Archimedes. Contains: On Sphere and Cylinder, Measurement of a Circle, Spirals, Conoids, Spheroids, etc. Definitive edition of greatest mathematical intellect of ancient world. 186 page study by Heath discusses Archimedes and history of Greek mathematics. 563pp. 5⅜ x 8.　S9 Paperbound **$2.00**

COLLECTED WORKS OF BERNARD RIEMANN. Important sourcebook, first to contain complete text of 1892 "Werke" and the 1902 supplement, unabridged. 31 monographs, 3 complete lecture courses, 15 miscellaneous papers which have been of enormous importance in relativity, topology, theory of complex variables, other areas of mathematics. Edited by R. Dedekind, H. Weber, M. Noether, W. Wirtinger. German text; English introduction by Hans Lewy. 690pp. 5⅜ x 8.　S226 Paperbound **$2.85**

THE THIRTEEN BOOKS OF EUCLID'S ELEMENTS, edited by Sir Thomas Heath. Definitive edition of one of very greatest classics of Western world. Complete translation of Heiberg text, plus spurious Book XIV. 150 page introduction on Greek, Medieval mathematics, Euclid, texts, commentators, etc. Elaborate critical apparatus parallels text, analyzing each definition, postulate, proposition, covering textual matters, refutations, supports, extrapolations, etc. This is the full Euclid. Unabridged reproduction of Cambridge U. 2nd edition. 3 volumes. 995 figures. 1426pp. 5⅜ x 8.　S88, 89, 90, 3 volume set, paperbound **$6.00**

AN INTRODUCTION TO GEOMETRY OF N DIMENSIONS, D. M. Y. Sommerville. Presupposes no previous knowledge of field. Only book in English devoted exclusively to higher dimensional geometry. Discusses fundamental ideas of incidence, parallelism, perpendicularity, angles between linear space, enumerative geometry, analytical geometry from projective and metric views, polytopes, elementary ideas in analysis situs, content of hyperspacial figures. 60 diagrams. 196pp. 5⅜ x 8.　S494 Paperbound **$1.50**

ELEMENTS OF NON-EUCLIDEAN GEOMETRY, D. M. Y. Sommerville. Unique in proceeding step-by-step. Requires only good knowledge of high-school geometry and algebra, to grasp elementary hyperbolic, elliptic, analytic non-Euclidean Geometries; space curvature and its implications; radical axes; homopethic centres and systems of circles; parataxy and parallelism; Gauss' proof of defect area theorem; much more, with exceptional clarity. 126 problems at chapter ends. 133 figures. xvi + 274pp. 5⅜ x 8.　S460 Paperbound **$1.50**

THE FOUNDATIONS OF EUCLIDEAN GEOMETRY, H. G. Forder. First connected, rigorous account in light of modern analysis, establishing propositions without recourse to empiricism, without multiplying hypotheses. Based on tools of 19th and 20th century mathematicians, who made it possible to remedy gaps and complexities, recognize problems not earlier discerned. Begins with important relationship of number systems in geometrical figures. Considers classes, relations, linear order, natural numbers, axioms for magnitudes, groups, quasi-fields, fields, non-Archimedean systems, the axiom system (at length), particular axioms (two chapters on the Parallel Axioms), constructions, congruence, similarity, etc. Lists: axioms employed, constructions, symbols in frequent use. 295pp. 5⅜ x 8.　S481 Paperbound **$2.00**

CALCULUS, FUNCTION THEORY (REAL AND COMPLEX), FOURIER THEORY

FIVE VOLUME "THEORY OF FUNCTIONS" SET BY KONRAD KNOPP. Provides complete, readily followed account of theory of functions. Proofs given concisely, yet without sacrifice of completeness or rigor. These volumes used as texts by such universities as M.I.T., Chicago, N.Y. City College, many others. "Excellent introduction . . . remarkably readable, concise, clear, rigorous," J. of the American Statistical Association.

ELEMENTS OF THE THEORY OF FUNCTIONS, Konrad Knopp. Provides background for further volumes in this set, or texts on similar level. Partial contents: Foundations, system of complex numbers and Gaussian plane of numbers, Riemann sphere of numbers, mapping by linear functions, normal forms, the logarithm, cyclometric functions, binomial series. "Not only for the young student, but also for the student who knows all about what is in it," Mathematical Journal. 140pp. 5⅜ x 8.　S154 Paperbound **$1.35**

THEORY OF FUNCTIONS, PART I, Konrad Knopp. With volume II, provides coverage of basic concepts and theorems. Partial contents: numbers and points, functions of a complex variable, integral of a continuous function, Cauchy's intergral theorem, Cauchy's integral formulae, series with variable terms, expansion and analytic function in a power series, analytic continuation and complete definition of analytic functions, Laurent expansion, types of singularities. vii + 146pp. 5⅜ x 8.　S156 Paperbound **$1.35**

THEORY OF FUNCTIONS, PART II, Konrad Knopp. Application and further development of general theory, special topics. Single valued functions, entire, Weierstrass. Meromorphic functions: Mittag-Leffler. Periodic functions. Multiple valued functions. Riemann surfaces. Algebraic functions. Analytical configurations, Riemann surface. x + 150pp. 5⅜ x 8.　S157 Paperbound **$1.35**

PROBLEM BOOK IN THE THEORY OF FUNCTIONS, VOLUME I, Konrad Knopp. Problems in elementary theory, for use with Knopp's "Theory of Functions," or any other text. Arranged according to increasing difficulty. Fundamental concepts, sequences of numbers and infinite series, complex variable, integral theorems, development in series, conformal mapping. Answers. viii + 126pp. 5⅜ x 8. **S 158 Paperbound $1.35**

PROBLEM BOOK IN THE THEORY OF FUNCTIONS, VOLUME II, Konrad Knopp. Advanced theory of functions, to be used with Knopp's "Theory of Functions," or comparable text. Singularities, entire and meromorphic functions, periodic, analytic, continuation, multiple-valued functions, Riemann surfaces, conformal mapping. Includes section of elementary problems. "The difficult task of selecting . . . problems just within the reach of the beginner is here masterfully accomplished," AM. MATH. SOC. Answers. 138pp. 5⅜ x 8.
S159 Paperbound $1.35

ADVANCED CALCULUS, E. B. Wilson. Still recognized as one of most comprehensive, useful texts. Immense amount of well-represented, fundamental material, including chapters on vector functions, ordinary differential equations, special functions, calculus of variations, etc., which are excellent introductions to these areas. Requires only one year of calculus. Over 1300 exercises cover both pure math and applications to engineering and physical problems. Ideal reference, refresher. 54 page introductory review. ix + 566pp. 5⅜ x 8.
S504 Paperbound $2.45

LECTURES ON THE THEORY OF ELLIPTIC FUNCTIONS, H. Hancock. Reissue of only book in English with so extensive a coverage, especially of Abel, Jacobi, Legendre, Weierstrass, Hermite, Liouville, and Riemann. Unusual fullness of treatment, plus applications as well as theory in discussing universe of elliptic integrals, originating in works of Abel and Jacobi. Use is made of Riemann to provide most general theory. 40-page table of formulas. 76 figures. xxiii + 498pp. 5⅜ x 8. **S483 Paperbound $2.55**

THEORY OF FUNCTIONALS AND OF INTEGRAL AND INTEGRO-DIFFERENTIAL EQUATIONS, Vito Volterra. Unabridged republication of only English translation. General theory of functions depending on continuous set of values of another function. Based on author's concept of transition from finite number of variables to a continually infinite number. Includes much material on calculus of variations. Begins with fundamentals, examines generalization of analytic functions, functional derivative equations, applications, other directions of theory, etc. New introduction by G. C. Evans. Biography, criticism of Volterra's work by E. Whittaker. xxxx + 226pp. 5⅜ x 8. **S502 Paperbound $1.75**

AN INTRODUCTION TO FOURIER METHODS AND THE LAPLACE TRANSFORMATION, Philip Franklin. Concentrates on essentials, gives broad view, suitable for most applications. Requires only knowledge of calculus. Covers complex qualities with methods of computing elementary functions for complex values of argument and finding approximations by charts; Fourier series; harmonic anaylsis; much more. Methods are related to physical problems of heat flow, vibrations, electrical transmission, electromagnetic radiation, etc. 828 problems, answers. Formerly entitled "Fourier Methods." x + 289pp. 5⅜ x 8.
S452 Paperbound $1.75

THE ANALYTICAL THEORY OF HEAT, Joseph Fourier. This book, which revolutionized mathematical physics, has been used by generations of mathematicians and physicists interested in heat or application of Fourier integral. Covers cause and reflection of rays of heat, radiant heating, heating of closed spaces, use of trigonometric series in theory of heat, Fourier integral, etc. Translated by Alexander Freeman. 20 figures. xxii + 466pp. 5⅜ x 8.
S93 Paperbound $2.00

ELLIPTIC INTEGRALS, H. Hancock. Invaluable in work involving differential equations with cubics, quatrics under root sign, where elementary calculus methods are inadequate. Practical solutions to problems in mathematics, engineering, physics; differential equations requiring integration of Lamé's, Briot's, or Bouquet's equations; determination of arc of ellipse, hyperbola, lemiscate; solutions of problems in elastics; motion of a projectile under resistance varying as the cube of the velocity; pendulums; more. Exposition in accordance with Legendre-Jacobi theory. Rigorous discussion of Legendre transformations. 20 figures. 5 place table. 104pp. 5⅜ x 8. **S484 Paperbound $1.25**

THE TAYLOR SERIES, AN INTRODUCTION TO THE THEORY OF FUNCTIONS OF A COMPLEX VARIABLE, P. Dienes. Uses Taylor series to approach theory of functions, using ordinary calculus only, except in last 2 chapters. Starts with introduction to real variable and complex algebra, derives properties of infinite series, complex differentiation, integration, etc. Covers biuniform mapping, overconvergence and gap theorems, Taylor series on its circle of convergence, etc. Unabridged corrected reissue of first edition. 186 examples, many fully worked out. 67 figures. xii + 555pp. 5⅜ x 8. **S391 Paperbound $2.75**

LINEAR INTEGRAL EQUATIONS, W. V. Lovitt. Systematic survey of general theory, with some application to differential equations, calculus of variations, problems of math, physics. Includes: integral equation of 2nd kind by successive substitutions; Fredholm's equation as ratio of 2 integral series in lambda, applications of the Fredholm theory, Hilbert-Schmidt theory of symmetric kernels, application, etc. Neumann, Dirichlet, vibratory problems. ix + 253pp. 5⅜ x 8. **S175 Clothbound $3.50**
S176 Paperbound $1.60

DOVER SCIENCE BOOKS

DICTIONARY OF CONFORMAL REPRESENTATIONS, H. Kober. Developed by British Admiralty to solve Laplace's equation in 2 dimensions. Scores of geometrical forms and transformations for electrical engineers, Joukowski aerofoil for aerodynamics, Schwartz-Christoffel transformations for hydro-dynamics, transcendental functions. Contents classified according to analytical functions describing transformations with corresponding regions. Glossary. Topological index. 447 diagrams. 6⅛ x 9¼. .S160 Paperbound **$2.00**

ELEMENTS OF THE THEORY OF REAL FUNCTIONS, J. E. Littlewood. Based on lectures at Trinity College, Cambridge, this book has proved extremely successful in introducing graduate students to modern theory of functions. Offers full and concise coverage of classes and cardinal numbers, well ordered series, other types of series, and elements of the theory of sets of points. 3rd revised edition. vii + 71pp. 5⅜ x 8. S171 Clothbound **$2.85**
S172 Paperbound **$1.25**

INFINITE SEQUENCES AND SERIES, Konrad Knopp. 1st publication in any language. Excellent introduction to 2 topics of modern mathematics, designed to give student background to penetrate further alone. Sequences and sets, real and complex numbers, etc. Functions of a real and complex variable. Sequences and series. Infinite series. Convergent power series. Expansion of elementary functions. Numerical evaluation of series. v + 186pp. 5⅜ x 8. S152 Clothbound **$3.50**
S153 Paperbound **$1.75**

THE THEORY AND FUNCTIONS OF A REAL VARIABLE AND THE THEORY OF FOURIER'S SERIES, E. W .Hobson. One of the best introductions to set theory and various aspects of functions and Fourier's series. Requires only a good background in calculus. Exhaustive coverage of: metric and descriptive properties of sets of points; transfinite numbers and order types; functions of a real variable; the Riemann and Lebesgue integrals; sequences and series of numbers; power-series; functions representable by series sequences of continuous functions; trigonometrical series; representation of functions by Fourier's series; and much more. "The best possible guide," Nature. Vol. I: 88 detailed examples, 10 figures. Index. xv + 736pp. Vol. II: 117 detailed examples, 13 figures. x + 780pp. 6⅛ x 9¼.
Vol. I: S387 Paperbound **$3.00**
Vol. II: S388 Paperbound **$3.00**

ALMOST PERIODIC FUNCTIONS, A. S. Besicovitch. Unique and important summary by a well known mathematician covers in detail the two stages of development in Bohr's theory of almost periodic functions: (1) as a generalization of pure periodicity, with results and proofs; (2) the work done by Stepanof, Wiener, Weyl, and Bohr in generalizing the theory. xi + 180pp. 5⅜ x 8. S18 Paperbound **$1.75**

INTRODUCTION TO THE THEORY OF FOURIER'S SERIES AND INTEGRALS, H. S. Carslaw. 3rd revised edition, an outgrowth of author's courses at Cambridge. Historical introduction, rational, irrational numbers, infinite sequences and series, functions of a single variable, definite integral, Fourier series, and similar topics. Appendices discuss practical harmonic analysis, periodogram analysis, Lebesgue's theory. 84 examples. xiii + 368pp. 5⅜ x 8.
S48 Paperbound **$2.00**

SYMBOLIC LOGIC

THE ELEMENTS OF MATHEMATICAL LOGIC, Paul Rosenbloom. First publication in any language. For mathematically mature readers with no training in symbolic logic. Development of lectures given at Lund Univ., Sweden, 1948. Partial contents: Logic of classes, fundamental theorems, Boolean algebra, logic of propositions, of propositional functions, expressive languages, combinatory logics, development of math within an object language, paradoxes, theorems of Post, Goedel, Church, and similar topics. iv + 214pp. 5⅜ x 8.
S227 Paperbound **$1.45**

INTRODUCTION TO SYMBOLIC LOGIC AND ITS APPLICATION, R. Carnap. Clear, comprehensive, rigorous, by perhaps greatest living master. Symbolic languages analyzed, one constructed. Applications to math (axiom systems for set theory, real, natural numbers), topology (Dedekind, Cantor continuity explanations), physics (general analysis of determination, causality, space-time topology), biology (axiom system for basic concepts). "A masterpiece," Zentralblatt für Mathematik und Ihre Grenzgebiete. Over 300 exercises. 5 figures. xvi + 241pp. 5⅜ x 8. S453 Paperbound **$1.85**

AN INTRODUCTION TO SYMBOLIC LOGIC, Susanne K. Langer. Probably clearest book for the philosopher, scientist, layman—no special knowledge of math required. Starts with simplest symbols, goes on to give remarkable grasp of Boole-Schroeder, Russell-Whitehead systems, clearly, quickly. Partial Contents: Forms, Generalization, Classes, Deductive System of Classes, Algebra of Logic, Assumptions of Principia Mathematica, Logistics, Proofs of Theorems, etc. "Clearest . . . simplest introduction . . . the intelligent non-mathematician should have no difficulty," MATHEMATICS GAZETTE. Revised, expanded 2nd edition. Truth-value tables. 368pp. 5⅜ 8. S164 Paperbound **$1.75**

TRIGONOMETRICAL SERIES, Antoni Zygmund. On modern advanced level. Contains carefully organized analyses of trigonometric, orthogonal, Fourier systems of functions, with clear adequate descriptions of summability of Fourier series, proximation theory, conjugate series, convergence, divergence of Fourier series. Especially valuable for Russian, Eastern European coverage. 329pp. 5⅜ x 8. S290 Paperbound **$1.50**

THE LAWS OF THOUGHT, George Boole. This book founded symbolic logic some 100 years ago. It is the 1st significant attempt to apply logic to all aspects of human endeavour. Partial contents: derivation of laws, signs and laws, interpretations, eliminations, conditions of a perfect method, analysis, Aristotelian logic, probability, and similar topics. xvii + 424pp. 5⅜ x 8. S28 Paperbound **$2.00**

SYMBOLIC LOGIC, C. I. Lewis, C. H. Langford. 2nd revised edition of probably most cited book in symbolic logic. Wide coverage of entire field; one of fullest treatments of paradoxes; plus much material not available elsewhere. Basic to volume is distinction between logic of extensions and intensions. Considerable emphasis on converse substitution, while matrix system presents supposition of variety of non-Aristotelian logics. Especially valuable sections on strict limitations, existence theorems. Partial contents: Boole-Schroeder algebra; truth value systems, the matrix method; implication and deductibility; general theory of propositions; etc. "Most valuable," Times, London. 506pp. 5⅜ x 8. S170 Paperbound **$2.00**

GROUP THEORY AND LINEAR ALGEBRA, SETS, ETC.

LECTURES ON THE ICOSAHEDRON AND THE SOLUTION OF EQUATIONS OF THE FIFTH DEGREE, Felix Klein. Solution of quintics in terms of rotations of regular icosahedron around its axes of symmetry. A classic, indispensable source for those interested in higher algebra, geometry, crystallography. Considerable explanatory material included. 230 footnotes, mostly bibliography. "Classical monograph . . . detailed, readable book," Math. Gazette. 2nd edition. xvi + 289pp. 5⅜ x 8. S314 Paperbound **$1.85**

INTRODUCTION TO THE THEORY OF GROUPS OF FINITE ORDER, R. Carmichael. Examines fundamental theorems and their applications. Beginning with sets, systems, permutations, etc., progresses in easy stages through important types of groups: Abelian, prime power, permutation, etc. Except 1 chapter where matrices are desirable, no higher math is needed. 783 exercises, problems. xvi + 447pp. 5⅜ x 8. S299 Clothbound **$3.95**
S300 Paperbound **$2.00**

THEORY OF GROUPS OF FINITE ORDER, W. Burnside. First published some 40 years ago, still one of clearest introductions. Partial contents: permutations, groups independent of representation, composition series of a group, isomorphism of a group with itself, Abelian groups, prime power groups, permutation groups, invariants of groups of linear substitution, graphical representation, etc. "Clear and detailed discussion . . . numerous problems which are instructive," Design News. xxiv + 512pp. 5⅜ x 8. S38 Paperbound **$2.45**

COMPUTATIONAL METHODS OF LINEAR ALGEBRA, V. N. Faddeeva, translated by C. D. Benster. 1st English translation of unique, valuable work, only one in English presenting systematic exposition of most important methods of linear algebra—classical, contemporary. Details of deriving numerical solutions of problems in mathematical physics. Theory and practice. Includes survey of necessary background, most important methods of solution, for exact, iterative groups. One of most valuable features is 23 tables, triple checked for accuracy, unavailable elsewhere. Translator's note. x + 252pp. 5⅜ x 8. S424 Paperbound **$1.95**

THE CONTINUUM AND OTHER TYPES OF SERIAL ORDER, E. V. Huntington. This famous book gives a systematic elementary account of the modern theory of the continuum as a type of serial order. Based on the Cantor-Dedekind ordinal theory, which requires no technical knowledge of higher mathematics, it offers an easily followed analysis of ordered classes, discrete and dense series, continuous series, Cantor's transfinite numbers. "Admirable introduction to the rigorous theory of the continuum . . . reading easy," Science Progress. 2nd edition. viii + 82pp. 5⅜ x 8. S129 Clothbound **$2.75**
S130 Paperbound **$1.00**

THEORY OF SETS, E. Kamke. Clearest, amplest introduction in English, well suited for independent study. Subdivisions of main theory, such as theory of sets of points, are discussed, but emphasis is on general theory. Partial contents: rudiments of set theory, arbitrary sets, their cardinal numbers, ordered sets, their order types, well-ordered sets, their cardinal numbers. vii + 144pp. 5⅜ x 8. S141 Paperbound **$1.35**

CONTRIBUTIONS TO THE FOUNDING OF THE THEORY OF TRANSFINITE NUMBERS, Georg Cantor. These papers founded a new branch of mathematics. The famous articles of 1895-7 are translated, with an 82-page introduction by P. E. B. Jourdain dealing with Cantor, the background of his discoveries, their results, future possibilities. ix + 211pp. 5⅜ x 8. S45 Paperbound **$1.25**

NUMERICAL AND GRAPHICAL METHODS, TABLES

JACOBIAN ELLIPTIC FUNCTION TABLES, L. M. Milne-Thomson. Easy-to-follow, practical, not only useful numerical tables, but complete elementary sketch of application of elliptic functions. Covers description of principle properties; complete elliptic integrals; Fourier series, expansions; periods, zeros, poles, residues, formulas for special values of argument; cubic, quartic polynomials; pendulum problem; etc. Tables, graphs form body of book: Graph, 5 figure table of elliptic function sn (u m); cn (u m); dn (u m). 8 figure table of complete elliptic integrals K, K′, E, E′, nome q. 7 figure table of Jacobian zeta-function Z(u). 3 figures. xi + 123pp. 5⅜ x 8.   S194 Paperbound **$1.35**

TABLES OF FUNCTIONS WITH FORMULAE AND CURVES, E. Jahnke, F. Emde. Most comprehensive 1-volume English text collection of tables, formulae, curves of transcendent functions. 4th corrected edition, new 76-page section giving tables, formulae for elementary functions not in other English editions. Partial contents: sine, cosine, logarithmic integral; error integral; elliptic integrals; theta functions; Legendre, Bessel, Riemann, Mathieu, hypergeometric functions; etc. "Out-of-the-way functions for which we know no other source." Scientific Computing Service, Ltd. 212 figures. 400pp. 5⅝ x 8⅜.   S133 Paperbound **$2.00**

MATHEMATICAL TABLES, H. B. Dwight. Covers in one volume almost every function of importance in applied mathematics, engineering, physical sciences. Three extremely fine tables of the three trig functions, inverses, to 1000th of radian; natural, common logs; squares, cubes; hyperbolic functions, inverses; $(a^2 + b^2)$ exp. ½a; complete elliptical integrals of 1st, 2nd kind; sine, cosine integrals; exponential integrals; $Ei(x)$ and $Ei(-x)$; binomial coefficients; factorials to 250; surface zonal harmonics, first derivatives; Bernoulli, Euler numbers, their logs to base of 10; Gamma function; normal probability integral; over 60pp. Bessel functions; Riemann zeta function. Each table with formulae generally used, sources of more extensive tables, interpolation data, etc. Over half have columns of differences, to facilitate interpolation. viii + 231pp. 5⅜ x 8.   S445 Paperbound **$1.75**

PRACTICAL ANALYSIS, GRAPHICAL AND NUMERICAL METHODS, F. A. Willers. Immensely practical hand-book for engineers. How to interpolate, use various methods of numerical differentiation and integration, determine roots of a single algebraic equation, system of linear equations, use empirical formulas, integrate differential equations, etc. Hundreds of shortcuts for arriving at numerical solutions. Special section on American calculating machines, by T. W. Simpson. Translation by R. T. Beyer. 132 illustrations. 422pp. 5⅜ x 8.
S273 Paperbound **$2.00**

NUMERICAL SOLUTIONS OF DIFFERENTIAL EQUATIONS, H. Levy, E. A. Baggott. Comprehensive collection of methods for solving ordinary differential equations of first and higher order. 2 requirements: practical, easy to grasp; more rapid than school methods. Partial contents: graphical integration of differential equations, graphical methods for detailed solution. Numerical solution. Simultaneous equations and equations of 2nd and higher orders. "Should be in the hands of all in research and applied mathematics, teaching," Nature. 21 figures. viii + 238pp. 5⅜ x 8.   S168 Paperbound **$1.75**

NUMERICAL INTEGRATION OF DIFFERENTIAL EQUATIONS, Bennet, Milne, Bateman. Unabridged republication of original prepared for National Research Council. New methods of integration by 3 leading mathematicians: "The Interpolational Polynomial," "Successive Approximation," A. A. Bennett, "Step-by-step Methods of Integration," W. W. Milne. "Methods for Partial Differential Equations," H. Bateman. Methods for partial differential equations, solution of differential equations to non-integral values of a parameter will interest mathematicians, physicists. 288 footnotes, mostly bibliographical. 235 item classified bibliography. 108pp. 5⅜ x 8.   S305 Paperbound **$1.35**

Write for free catalogs!

Indicate your field of interest. Dover publishes books on physics, earth sciences, mathematics, engineering, chemistry, astronomy, anthropology, biology, psychology, philosophy, religion, history, literature, mathematical recreations, languages, crafts, art, graphic arts, etc.

Write to Dept. catr
Dover Publications, Inc.
Science A   *180 Varick St., N. Y. 14, N. Y.*